Also from An

"A quick look at" series

The "A quick look at" series of short straight-to-the-point books about emotion, communication and relationship topics, includes:

Demystifying Emotions,
Anxiety, and
Talking with Tact.

Hypnosis Recordings

Hypnosis can be helpful for releasing emotional baggage and improving how you deal with challenging emotions. My *Release & Refresh* emotional detox hypnosis helps you let go of anything that has burdened, stressed, or overwhelmed you. It helps release any thoughts and feelings that have held you back or kept you stuck.

Journal/Workbooks and Activity Books

Learn, Let Go, Lighten Up: Silver Lining Emotional Detox Journal & Workbook helps you work through anything that burdens or overwhelms you, or gets in the way of you reaching your potential.

Coming soon: other journal/workbooks and emotional intelligence boosting activity books for adults, teens, and children.

Visit annsilvers.com often for the ever-expanding list of self-help products.

Increasing My HAPPINESS QUOTIENT

Silver Lining Joy Journal & Workbook

Ann Silvers, MA

SILVERSPUBLISHING

ISBN: 978-1-948551-01-4

Printed in the United States of America
8 7 6 5 4 3 2 1

Published by Silvers Publishing, LLC
Gig Harbor, WA, USA
silverspublishing.com

Contents

Preface

Your Happiness Quotient (HQ) is your ability to be happy and feel joy. It's the feel-good side of Emotional Intelligence. It's not a stagnant thing. It's a skill you can develop and nurture.

Joy isn't dependent on wealth or vacations in far-off lands (though I'm not knocking those things), it's about noticing the happies big and small, and being able to be nourished by those moments. It's more about where you are mentally and emotionally than where you are financially and geographically.

In working with my counseling and coaching clients, I've realized that happiness is a skill that not everyone has. This spurred me on to think about how I happened to be a happy person even though I by no means came from happy circumstances. Over the years, that self-examination, as well as research and experimentation, led to this journal.

Creating this journal has been one of my most favorite projects ever! Putting the exercises—like Bonus Smiles and Bonus Laughs—into practice myself has added joy to my days and I hope it will bump up your HQ too (whether you are a joy novice or expert).

Happy journaling,

–Ann Silvers

Increasing My
**HAPPINESS
QUOTIENT**

Silver Lining
Joy Journal
& Workbook

Ann Silvers, MA

DIY Journal Add-ons

If you prefer spiral binding for your journals,
you may have a local print shop or copy store that
will convert this journal to a spiral version.

You can also add your own ribbon page-keepers
by taping the ends of a couple of ribbon strips
to the inside back cover.

Getting Started

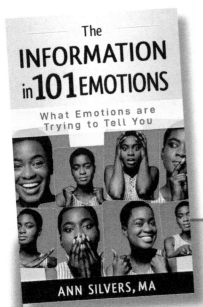

This *Silver Lining Joy Journal & Workbook* is here to help you develop the skill of happiness, increase your Happiness Quotient (HQ) and have some fun along the way. It will help you:

- focus on your feel-good emotions and learn how to get the information and nourishment they have to offer,
- build happiness skills,
- notice your small smilables, and
- get bonus smiles and laughs to make your life lighter and brighter.

I've even included games and stretches! :)

Daily pages

The journal/workbook has both variety and continuity. Each day's pages provide writing prompts or activities based on rotating themes and also a reoccurring section for entering daily happiness highlights.

Each day, you are offered prompts and simple thought-provoking activities to boost your HQ using a rotation of themes:

- Every second set of pages focuses on a feel-good emotion*
- *Reflection* offers an HQ-boosting quote to reflect on and write about
- *Stretch Day* teaches something new
- *Game Day* puzzles are a fun way to nudge up your HQ
- *Check-in Day* helps you review what you're learning, how you're doing, and plan for increased happiness

*The fifty feel-good "comfortable" emotions are drawn from the list of 101 emotions I use to teach emotion skills. The whole list is on the next page as a reference for you. (The 101 emotions are also included in my *Emotional Intelligence Booster* card set available at annsilvers.com.)

At the bottom of each page there is a section for tracking *Happiness Highlights*: small and large joys of the day. This section has prompts added to it as HQ-building skills are introduced.

Happiness Highlights

Small
Smilables

101 Emotions

Accepted	Content	Included	Respected
Acknowledged	Creative	Independent	Safe
Amused	Curious	Inspired	Satisfied
Appreciated	Delighted	Interested	Secure
Attracted	Empowered	Liberated	Stimulated
Attractive	Encouraged	Loved	Supported
Calm	Enthusiastic	Nurtured	Surprised *
Capable	Excited	Passionate	Trusted
Caring	Exhilarated	Protected	Trusting
Competent	Grateful	Proud	Understood
Confident	Happy	Reassured	Valued
Connected	Hopeful	Relaxed	Welcome
Considered	Important	Relieved	

Abandoned	Disappointed	Inferior	Rejected
Afraid	Disconnected	Insecure	Resentful
(Angry) **	Discounted	Jealous	Sad
Anxious	Discouraged	Lonely	Shame
Belittled	Disrespected	Manipulated	Shocked
Betrayed	Embarrassed	Nervous	Surprised *
Concerned	Excluded	Obligated	Trapped
Confused	Foolish	Offended	Unappreciated
Controlled	Frustrated	Overwhelmed	Unattractive
Deceived	Grief	Panic	Violated
Defeated	Guilty	Powerless	Vulnerable
Defensive	Humiliated	Pressured	Worried
Devastated	Inadequate	Regret	

*Surprised is an example of an emotion that is sometimes comfortable and sometimes uncomfortable.

**Angry is usually a secondary emotion, some other uncomfortable emotion(s) is/are under the anger.

"I" messages

Throughout the journal, you are often prompted to use the "I" message formula for expressing your thoughts and feelings. An "I" message is a great way to talk to yourself for clarity and to talk to others with tact.

Using the "I" messages in the journal helps you take in and absorb the information in your feel-good emotions, sort out why you feel what you feel, and also practice using the formula so you can boost your ability to process your emotions as they come up in real-time.

The basic "I" message formula is:

I feel/felt ___*emotion*___ when _____*situation*_____
because _____*reason*_____ .

For example:

I felt ___*appreciated*___ when ___*they thanked me for making dinner*___
because ___*then I knew they recognized my effort*___ .

For more info about "I" messages check out my booklet, *A quick look at Demystifying Emotions,* at annsilvers.com and online retailers like Amazon.

This is your journal.
Give yourself permission to skip around
if you feel like it.

A few pages of note about explanations
connected to tracking daily happinesses:

Happiness Highlights: p. 3
Bonus Smiles: p. 14/15
Small Smilables: p. 22/23
Bonus Laughs: p. 38/39

Daily Pages

Happy

The message in "happy" is:
I feel good.
(It's a general feeling, but it's a good place to start.)

Think of a time you felt happy and complete this "I" message.

I felt happy when _____

_____

_____

because _____

_____

_____

Describe that situation or event.

_____

_____

_____

_____

_____

Close your eyes and take yourself back to that event.
Notice the happy feeling.
Breathe in that feeling as if you are breathing it in to the core of
you. From the core of you, let it spread out and fill you up.
Savor the feeling.

Happiness Highlights

Happy

List 3 times you felt happy
(even if it was just a little happy).

1. _____

2. _____

3. _____

Make a general "I" message about feeling happy.

I feel happy when _____

_____

_____

because _____

_____

_____.

What helps me feel happy?

_____

_____

_____

_____

_____

_____

_____

_____

Happiness Highlights

Reflection

"Humor and joy are skills,
not the luck of the draw."

– C. W. Metcalf,
Lighten Up: Survival Skills for People Under Pressure

_____

_____

_____

_____

_____

_____

_____

_____

_____

_____

_____

_____

_____

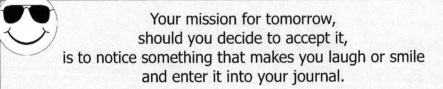

Your mission for tomorrow,
should you decide to accept it,
is to notice something that makes you laugh or smile
and enter it into your journal.

Happiness Highlights

Date _____

Reflection, Part Two

Something that made me laugh or smile

Write about something that made you smile or laugh today.

(If nothing made you smile today, write about something that made you smile or laugh in the past.)

_____

_____

_____

_____

_____

_____

What helped or got in the way of you smiling today?

_____

_____

_____

_____

_____

_____

_____

_____

_____

Happiness Highlights

Encouraged

The message in "encouraged" is:
I'm feeling more like I should or can do something
than I did before.

Think of a time you felt encouraged and complete this "I" message.

I felt encouraged when _____

_____

_____

because _____

_____

_____

Describe that situation or event.

_____

_____

_____

_____

_____

 Close your eyes and take yourself back to that event.
Notice the encouraged feeling.
Breathe in that feeling as if you are breathing it in to the core of
you. From the core of you, let it spread out and fill you up.
Savor the feeling.

Happiness Highlights

Date _____

Su Mo Tu We Th Fr Sa

Encouraged

List 3 times you felt encouraged
(even if it was just a little encouraged).

1. _____

2. _____

3. _____

How do people encourage others?

_____

_____

_____

_____

How have people encouraged me?

_____

_____

_____

_____

How can I encourage myself?

_____

_____

_____

_____

_____

Happiness Highlights

Stretch Day

Up your smile count with smiles

Research shows that even fake smiles improve your mood, reduce physical pain, and increase stress-resistance.

Give it a go: fake smile for at least 15 seconds
and note what you notice.

_____

_____

_____

_____

Where in my day can I fit in some bonus smiles? (ie when you wake up, in the shower, while driving or riding the bus, standing in line, waiting on hold, each time you dry your hands . . .)

1. _____
2. _____
3. _____
4. _____
5. _____

> Your mission for tomorrow,
> should you decide to accept it,
> is to fit in 3 bonus consciously-initiated un-spontaneous
> smiles and note them in your journal.

Happiness Highlights

Date _____

Stretch Day, The Sequel

 smiles

The bonus smiles I fit in today:

1. _____

2. _____

3. _____

My experience with consciously initiating smiles:

_____

_____

_____

_____

_____

_____

My bonus smile plan for tomorrow/future:

_____

_____

_____

_____

Noting how many bonus smiles you had, or just putting a check mark showing that you had at least one, can help you remember to get them into your day. (And it can give you another smile as you recount it.)

Track Bonus smiles here after today

Happiness Highlights

15

Curious

The message in "curious" is:
I wonder about something.

Think of a time you felt curious and complete this "I" message.

I felt curious when _____

_____

_____

because _____

_____

_____ .

Describe that situation or event.

_____

_____

_____

_____

_____

_____

_____

Close your eyes and take yourself back to that event.
Notice the curious feeling.
Breathe in that feeling as if you are breathing it in to the core of
you. From the core of you, let it spread out and fill you up.
Savor the feeling.

Happiness Highlights

Bonus! ☺

Date _____

Curious

List 3 times you felt curious
(even if it was just a little curious).

1. _____

2. _____

3. _____

Make a general "I" message about feeling curious.

I feel curious when _____

_____

_____

because _____

_____

_____ .

What have I accomplished when I felt curious?

_____

_____

_____

_____

_____

_____

_____

_____

Happiness Highlights

Bonus! ☺

Game Day Word Search

Words can be forwards, backwards, up, down, or diagonal.

```
D  F  P  D  O  O  T  S  R  E  D  N  U  H
G  E  E  N  T  H  U  S  I  A  S  T  I  C
K  M  X  L  R  Q  R  M  K  V  E  N  G  P
W  F  N  A  Y  C  L  Z  C  N  F  F  D  M
N  Y  R  R  L  A  Y  V  X  W  A  Z  E  Z
I  T  K  N  C  E  L  K  L  K  S  H  T  R
N  L  B  H  H  G  R  U  B  M  H  X  P  N
D  K  D  N  D  T  F  D  U  O  R  P  E  W
E  X  C  I  T  E  D  C  G  V  N  T  C  N
P  G  G  B  T  C  V  H  M  H  X  R  C  W
E  V  T  A  L  T  K  E  O  C  Q  T  A  L
N  D  R  L  L  L  T  J  I  P  Z  H  O  M
D  G  G  D  M  G  W  R  L  L  E  V  B  R
E  T  H  N  N  Q  X  V  V  B  E  F  V  H
N  M  I  N  C  L  U  D  E  D  B  R  U  Y
T  F  Z  E  N  C  O  U  R  A  G  E  D  L
```

ACCEPTED	EXCITED	INDEPENDENT	SAFE
CALM	GRATEFUL	UNDERSTOOD	LOVED
ENCOURAGED	HOPEFUL	PROUD	RELIEVED
ENTHUSIASTIC	INCLUDED	RELAXED	

Happiness Highlights

Date _____

Check-in Day

Reflect back on what you've been learning
about upping your Happiness Quotient (HQ).

What are some HQ key points I've learned?

_____
_____
_____
_____
_____

What learning am I putting into action?

_____
_____
_____
_____
_____

My HQ-boosting plan moving forward:

_____
_____
_____
_____
_____

Happiness Highlights

Bonus! ☺

Enthusiastic

The message in "enthusiastic" is:
I really want to do this.

Think of a time you felt enthusiastic and complete this "I" message.

I felt enthusiastic when _____

_____

_____

because _____

_____

_____

Describe that situation or event.

_____

_____

_____

_____

_____

_____

Close your eyes and take yourself back to that event.
Notice the enthusiastic feeling.
Breathe in that feeling as if you are breathing it in to the core of
you. From the core of you, let it spread out and fill you up.
Savor the feeling.

Happiness Highlights

Date _____

Enthusiastic

List 3 times you felt enthusiastic
(even if it was just a little enthusiastic).

1. _____

2. _____

3. _____

What do I feel enthusiastic about now?

_____

_____

_____

_____

_____

_____

How could I increase my enthusiasm?

_____

_____

_____

_____

_____

_____

_____

Happiness Highlights

Bonus! ☺

Reflection

"Recognize joy when it arrives in the plain brown
wrappings of everyday life."

-Judith Viorst

_____

_____

_____

_____

_____

_____

_____

_____

_____

_____

_____

_____

_____

Your mission for tomorrow, should you decide to accept
it, is to notice 3 small smilable things and enter them on
the next page. (ie: a sunset, green traffic light, mathematical
equation, something amusing or inspiring . . .)

Happiness Highlights

Date _____

Reflection, Part Two

Small Smilables

Small Smilables I noticed today:

1. _____

2. _____

3. _____

What I notice about the things I noticed:

_____

_____

_____

_____

_____

_____

How can I increase my smiles tomorrow?

_____

_____

_____

_____

_____

*Track
Small Smilables
here after today*

Happiness Highlights

Small
Smilables

Bonus! ☺

Relieved

The message in "relieved" is:
Phew. I'm glad that didn't happen or is over.

Think of a time you felt relieved and complete this "I" message.

I felt relieved when _____

_____

_____

because _____

_____

_____

Describe that situation or event.

_____

_____

_____

_____

_____

_____

Close your eyes and take yourself back to that event.
Notice the relieved feeling.
Breathe in that feeling as if you are breathing it in to the core of
you. From the core of you, let it spread out and fill you up.
Savor the feeling.

Happiness Highlights

Small
Smilables

Bonus!

Date _____

Relieved

List 3 times you felt relieved
(even if it was just a little relieved).

1. _____

2. _____

3. _____

Make a general "I" message about feeling relieved.

I feel relieved when _____

_____

_____

because _____

_____

_____ ,

Is there something happening now or in the future that I look forward to feeling relieved about?

_____

_____

_____

_____

_____

_____

_____

Happiness Highlights

Small
Smilables

Bonus! ☺

Stretch Day

Messages about being happy

Did I receive messages from my parents or anyone else that told me that I shouldn't be happy?

_____

_____

_____

_____

Do I fear happiness in any way?

_____

_____

_____

_____

What do I want to believe about happiness?

_____

_____

_____

_____

_____

_____

_____

_____

Happiness Highlights

Small
Smilables

Bonus! ☺

Date _____

Stretch Day, The Sequel

Messages about being happy

Make an "I" message for a time you felt fear about being happy. (If there was a time.)

I feel/felt scared about being happy when _____

_____

_____

because _____

_____

_____

What are the benefits of being happy?
(If you can't come up with 9, consider thinking about it over the next few days and adding to your list. Maybe do some research for ideas.)

1. _____
2. _____
3. _____
4. _____
5. _____
6. _____
7. _____
8. _____
9. _____

Happiness Highlights

Small
Smilables

Bonus! ☺

27

Excited

The message in "excited" is:
I <u>really</u> look forward to this or enjoy this.

Think of a time you felt excited and complete this "I" message.

I felt excited when _____

_____

_____

because _____

_____

_____ .

Describe that situation or event.

_____

_____

_____

_____

_____

_____

Close your eyes and take yourself back to that event.
Notice the excited feeling.
Breathe in that feeling as if you are breathing it in to the core of
you. From the core of you, let it spread out and fill you up.
Savor the feeling.

Happiness Highlights

Small
Smilables

Bonus!

Date _____

Excited

List 3 times you felt excited
(even if it was just a little excited).

1. _____
2. _____
3. _____

Make a general "I" message about feeling excited.

I feel excited when _____

_____

_____

because _____

_____

_____ '

What are some things I could do in the future that would be exciting?

_____

_____

_____

_____

_____

_____

_____

_____

Happiness Highlights

Small
Smilables

Bonus! ☺

Game Day

Words can be forwards, backwards, up, down, or diagonal.

```
M  R  R  G  D  E  T  C  E  T  O  R  P  W
C  L  V  N  E  Y  L  U  F  E  P  O  H  R
M  V  L  P  M  N  K  M  B  D  H  P  K  N
Q  T  Y  G  P  X  R  Z  O  A  X  N  R  P
P  D  R  K  O  Z  R  O  P  G  N  D  K  P
J  L  T  H  W  W  T  P  Q  R  M  E  L  G
L  T  H  T  E  S  Y  Y  N  A  J  T  B  D
N  D  L  D  R  R  K  D  H  T  D  P  P  E
B  K  E  E  E  C  O  M  P  E  T  E  N  T
P  L  D  L  D  D  P  P  R  F  H  C  M  S
M  N  M  J  I  L  U  U  M  U  V  C  X  U
U  D  Y  W  Q  G  S  L  B  L  M  A  W  R
B  E  K  H  B  S  H  J  C  Y  P  M  Y  T
B  V  Y  K  A  X  N  T  G  N  L  L  N  W
G  O  S  E  C  U  R  E  E  A  I  D  J  R
M  L  R  M  N  V  M  Z  C  D  T  M  N  T
```

ACCEPTED	GRATEFUL	EMPOWERED	SECURE
CALM	HAPPY	PROTECTED	TRUSTED
COMPETENT	HOPEFUL	UNDERSTOOD	INCLUDED
DELIGHTED	LOVED	REASSURED	

Happiness Highlights

Small
Smilables

Date _____

Check-in Day

Reflect back on what you've been learning
about upping your Happiness Quotient (HQ).

What are some HQ key points I've learned?

_____
_____
_____
_____
_____

What learning am I putting into action?

_____
_____
_____
_____
_____

My HQ-boosting plan moving forward:

_____
_____
_____
_____
_____
_____

Happiness Highlights

Small
Smilables

Bonus! ☺

Date _____
Su Mo Tu We Th Fr Sa

Inspired

The message in "inspired" is:
Someone or something raised my spirits,
helped me feel more like doing something.

Think of a time you felt inspired and complete this "I" message.

I felt inspired when _____

_____

_____

because _____

_____

_____ .

Describe that situation or event.

_____

_____

_____

_____

_____

Close your eyes and take yourself back to that event.
Notice the inspired feeling.
Breathe in that feeling as if you are breathing it in to the core of
you. From the core of you, let it spread out and fill you up.
Savor the feeling.

Happiness Highlights

Small
Smilables

Date _____

Inspired

List 3 times you felt inspired
(even if it was just a little inspired).

1. _____
2. _____
3. _____

What helps me feel inspired?

_____
_____
_____
_____
_____
_____
_____

What have I accomplished when I felt inspired?

_____
_____
_____
_____
_____
_____
_____
_____

Happiness Highlights

Small
Smilables

Bonus! ☺

Reflection

"From there to here, from here to there,
funny things are everywhere."

– Dr. Seuss

_____

_____

_____

_____

_____

_____

_____

_____

_____

_____

_____

_____

_____

Your mission for tomorrow,
should you decide to accept it,
is to notice something funny
and to note it in your journal.

Happiness Highlights

Small
Smilables

Reflection, Part Two

Something funny happened on my way to the . . .

Write about something funny that you noticed today.

_____

_____

_____

_____

_____

_____

_____

What did you learn from looking for something funny?

_____

_____

_____

_____

_____

_____

_____

_____

_____

Happiness Highlights

Small
Smilables

35

Date _____

Su Mo Tu We Th Fr Sa

Amused

The message in "amused" is:
Something or someone is somewhat funny.

Think of a time you felt amused and complete this "I" message.

I felt amused when _____

_____

_____

because _____

_____

_____

Describe that situation or event.

_____

_____

_____

_____

_____

Close your eyes and take yourself back to that event.
Notice the amused feeling.
Breathe in that feeling as if you are breathing it in to the core of
you. From the core of you, let it spread out and fill you up.
Savor the feeling.

Happiness Highlights

Small
Smilables

Bonus! ☺

36

Date _____

Su Mo Tu We Th Fr Sa

Amused

List 3 times you felt amused
(even if it was just a little amused).

1. _____
2. _____
3. _____

List some things/experiences that make you laugh.

1. _____
2. _____
3. _____
4. _____
5. _____
6. _____
7. _____
8. _____
9. _____

How can I get more laughter in my life?

_____

_____

_____

_____

_____

Happiness Highlights

Small
Smilables

Stretch Day

Up your laugh count with laughs

Laughter has many benefits to your body and mind: it increases your immune response, exercises your innards, and boosts your mood. You don't have to wait for something funny to cross your path to get a laugh. You can make laughter happen. There are many ways you can get laughter started. We'll do one bonus laughter exercise today and another tomorrow.

**Think about times you laughed in the past
and write about the biggest laugh you can remember.**

_____

_____

_____

_____

_____

_____

_____

_____

_____

**Now let yourself really get into that experience
and laugh out loud just thinking about how funny it was.
Keep the laugh going as long as you can.**

In the future, you can use thinking about this memory to help you add a laugh or two to your day.

Happiness Highlights

Small
Smilables

Date _____

Stretch Day, The Sequel

More laughs

For this laughing exercise stand with your feet planted on the floor
and your arms at your sides.

Raise up your arms as you say a stretched vowel (like eeeee or aaaaaa)
until you turn it into a giggle.

Wave your hands around as you let it become a fuller laugh.

Repeat the arm movements as often as you want.

Make the laugh as big and long as you can.

Write about your experience and how you can use it in the future
for bonus laughs. (After I did this once, I just have to think about it to get
my bonus laughter on.)

_____

_____

_____

_____

_____

_____

_____

_____

_____ Track
Bonus laughs
_____ here after today

_____

Happiness Highlights

Small
Smilables

Bonus! ☺ 😀 LOL!

39

Delighted

The message in "delighted" is:
I'm <u>very</u> happy about something.

Think of a time you felt delighted and complete this "I" message.

I felt delighted when _____

_____

_____

because _____

_____

_____

Describe that situation or event.

_____

_____

_____

_____

_____

_____

Close your eyes and take yourself back to that event.
Notice the delighted feeling.
Breathe in that feeling as if you are breathing it in to the core of
you. From the core of you, let it spread out and fill you up.
Savor the feeling.

Happiness Highlights

Small
Smilables

Bonus! ☺ ☺ LOL!

40

Date _____

Delighted

List 3 times you felt delighted
(even if it was just a little delighted).

1. _____

2. _____

3. _____

Make a general "I" message about feeling delighted.

I feel delighted when _____

_____

_____

because _____

_____

_____

How can I get more delight in my life?

_____

_____

_____

_____

_____

_____

_____

_____

Happiness Highlights

Small
Smilables

Bonus! ☺ 😊 LOL!

Game Day Word Play

Fill in the blanks using words from the word bank.

1. "Laughing deeply is _____ deeply." –Milan Kundera

2. "If it feels good to laugh, then _____ to feel good." –Mike Moore

3. "Laughter is a gift from nature. It's good for us. It's _____, easy to _____ around and we can _____ it with anyone." –Jeffrey Briar

4. "It is bad to _____ laughter. It goes back down and spreads to your _____." –Fred Allen

5. "Laughter is like changing a baby's _____ —it doesn't permanently solve any problems, _____ it makes things more _____ for a while." –Unknown

free	diaper	hips
but	carry	living
share	laugh	suppress
tolerable		

Happiness Highlights

Small
Smilables

Date _____

Check-in Day

Reflect back on what you've been learning
about upping your Happiness Quotient (HQ).

What are some HQ key points I've learned?

_____
_____
_____
_____

_____

What learning am I putting into action?

_____
_____
_____
_____

_____

My HQ-boosting plan moving forward:

_____
_____
_____
_____
_____

_____

Happiness Highlights

Small
Smilables

Bonus!

LOL!

43

Included

The message in "included" is:
Someone helped me be a part of something.

Think of a time you felt included and complete this "I" message.

I felt included when _____

_____

_____

because _____

_____

_____ .

Describe that situation or event.

_____

_____

_____

_____

_____

_____

Close your eyes and take yourself back to that event.
Notice the included feeling.
Breathe in that feeling as if you are breathing it in to the core of
you. From the core of you, let it spread out and fill you up.
Savor the feeling.

Happiness Highlights

Small
Smilables

Bonus! ☺ 😃 LOL!

Date _____

Included

List 3 times you felt included
(even if it was just a little included).

1. _____

2. _____

3. _____

Make a general "I" message about feeling included.

I feel included when _____

_____

_____

because _____

_____

_____

What helps me feel included?

_____

_____

_____

_____

_____

_____

_____

_____

Happiness Highlights

Small
Smilables

Bonus! ☺ ☺ LOL!

45

Reflection

"Caring about the happiness of others,
we find our own."

–Plato

_____

_____

_____

_____

_____

_____

_____

_____

_____

_____

_____

_____

_____

Your mission for tomorrow,
should you decide to accept it, is to look for
opportunities to give someone(s) small happy boosts
and write about your experience in your journal.

Happiness Highlights

Small
Smilables

Date _____
Su Mo Tu We Th Fr Sa

Reflection, Part Two

Happy Boosts

My experience of attempting to notice small things that might help someone(s) get a happiness boost:

_____
_____
_____
_____
_____
_____
_____

My happy booster plan for tomorrow/future:

_____
_____
_____
_____
_____
_____
_____
_____

Happiness Highlights

Small
Smilables

Bonus! 😊 😊 LOL!

Caring

The message in "caring" is:
I am concerned about someone or something
and want to help them.

Think of a time you felt caring and complete this "I" message.

I felt caring when _____

_____

_____

because _____

_____

_____

Describe that situation or event.

_____

_____

_____

_____

_____

Close your eyes and take yourself back to that event.
Notice the caring feeling.
Breathe in that feeling as if you are breathing it in to the core of
you. From the core of you, let it spread out and fill you up.
Savor the feeling.

Happiness Highlights

Small
Smilables

Bonus! 😊 😄 LOL!

Date _____

Caring

List 3 times you felt caring
(even if it was just a little caring).

1. _____
2. _____
3. _____

What helps me feel caring?

_____
_____
_____
_____
_____
_____

How can I be caring towards myself?

_____
_____
_____
_____
_____
_____
_____
_____

Happiness Highlights

Small
Smilables

Bonus! ☺ ☺ LOL!

Stretch Day

The positive side of mistakes

Make an "I" message about when you make a mistake.
(You may want to look back to the emotions list on page 4.)

I feel _____ when I make a mistake

because _____

_____

_____

_____

Reflect on this twist to a quote from Albert Einstein:
Show me *a* person who has never made a mistake
and I'll show you *the* person who has never made anything.

_____

_____

_____

_____

_____

_____

_____

_____

_____

_____

Happiness Highlights

Small
Smilables

Bonus! ☺ ☺ LOL!

50

Date _____
Su Mo Tu We Th Fr Sa

Stretch Day, The Sequel

The positive side of mistakes

Think of a time you made a mistake that you gained something from. What did you learn from the mistake?

The mistake: _____

The learning: _____

_____

_____

_____

_____

_____

Challenge your negative self-talk about mistakes
(I give you an example to get you started.)

negative message	counter message
"Better not make the wrong choice!"	"If I'm wrong I'll learn what doesn't work."

Happiness Highlights

Small
Smilables

Empowered

The message in "empowered" is:
Something or someone has made me think
"I can do it!"

Think of a time you felt empowered and complete this "I" message.

I felt empowered when _____

_____

_____

because _____

_____

_____ .

Describe that situation or event.

_____

_____

_____

_____

_____

_____

Close your eyes and take yourself back to that event.
Notice the empowered feeling.
Breathe in that feeling as if you are breathing it in to the core of
you. From the core of you, let it spread out and fill you up.
Savor the feeling.

Happiness Highlights

Small
Smilables

Bonus! 😊 😃 LOL!

52

Date _____

Su Mo Tu We Th Fr Sa

Empowered

List 3 times you felt empowered
(even if it was just a little empowered).

1. _____

2. _____

3. _____

Make a general "I" message about feeling empowered.

I feel empowered when _____

_____

_____

because _____

_____

_____ .

How can I empower myself?

_____

_____

_____

_____

_____

_____

_____

_____

Happiness Highlights

Small
Smilables

53

Date _____

Su Mo Tu We Th Fr Sa

Game Day, A Mazing

Find your way through the maze to join the dancing penguins. See how many different routes you can find. Try to find the longest and shortest.

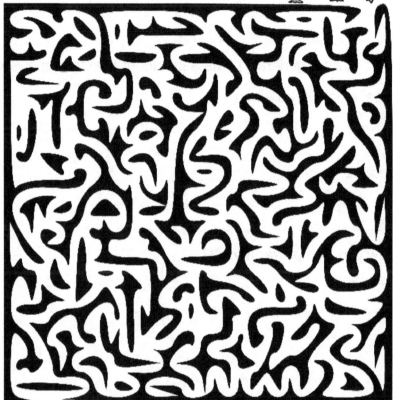

Just like the maze, there are many routes to happiness, some of them short, some longer, some are windier than others. . . Sometimes you have to backtrack, reroute or start over. Enjoy the journey.

Happiness Highlights

Small
Smilables

Date _____

Check-in Day

Reflect back on what you've been learning
about upping your Happiness Quotient (HQ).

What are some HQ key points I've learned?

_____
_____
_____
_____

What learning am I putting into action?

_____
_____
_____
_____

My HQ-boosting plan moving forward:

_____
_____
_____
_____
_____

Happiness Highlights

Small
Smilables

Bonus! ☺ ☺ LOL!

Competent

The message in "competent" is:
I can do this good enough.

Think of a time you felt competent and complete this "I" message.

I felt competent when _____

_____

_____

because _____

_____

_____ .

Describe that situation or event.

_____

_____

_____

_____

_____

_____

Close your eyes and take yourself back to that event.
Notice the competent feeling.
Breathe in that feeling as if you are breathing it in to the core of
you. From the core of you, let it spread out and fill you up.
Savor the feeling.

Happiness Highlights

Small
Smilables

Bonus! ☺ ☺ LOL!

56

Date _____

Competent

List 3 times you felt competent
(even if it was just a little competent).

1. _____

2. _____

3. _____

How does (or could) feeling competent help me?

_____

_____

_____

_____

Is there something going on now or coming up that I don't feel that competent about?

_____

_____

_____

_____

What could help me feel more competent?

_____

_____

_____

_____

Happiness Highlights

Small
Smilables

Bonus! ☺ ☺ LOL!

Reflection

"We ourselves feel that what we are doing is just a drop in the ocean. But the ocean would be less because of that missing drop."

– Mother Theresa

_____

_____

_____

_____

_____

_____

_____

_____

_____

_____

_____

_____

Your mission for tomorrow, should you decide to accept it, is to think about how you add drops to "the ocean": the small ways you add something to the lives of those around you.

Happiness Highlights

Small
Smilables

58

Reflection, Part Two

What I add

Small ways I add to the lives of people around me:

_____

_____

_____

_____

_____

_____

_____

Some small ways I could add to the lives of people around me, or within the reach of my influence, in the future:

_____

_____

_____

_____

_____

_____

_____

_____

_____

Happiness Highlights

Small
Smilables

Bonus! 😊 😊 LOL!

Safe

The message in "safe" is:
I'm <u>not</u> in danger.

Think of a time you felt safe and complete this "I" message.

I felt safe when _____

_____

_____

because _____

_____

_____ .

Describe that situation or event.

_____

_____

_____

_____

_____

_____

Close your eyes and take yourself back to that event.
Notice the safe feeling.
Breathe in that feeling as if you are breathing it in to the core of
you. From the core of you, let it spread out and fill you up.
Savor the feeling.

Happiness Highlights

Small
Smilables

Date _____
Su Mo Tu We Th Fr Sa

Safe

List 3 times you felt safe
(even if it was just a little safe).

1. _____
2. _____
3. _____

Make a general "I" message about feeling safe.

I feel safe when _____

_____

_____

because _____

_____

_____

What helps me feel safe?

_____

_____

_____

_____

_____

_____

_____

_____

Happiness Highlights

Small
Smilables

Bonus!

61

Stretch Day

Stretching your comfort zone

"Whenever we take a chance and enter unfamiliar territory or put ourselves into the world in a new way, we experience fear. Very often this fear keeps us from moving ahead in our lives."

– Susan Jeffers,
Feel the Fear and Do It Anyway

How does fear confine me?

_____
_____
_____
_____
_____

What can I do tomorrow to stretch my comfort zone, even a little? (i.e. talk to someone new, eat something different, start a project you've been putting off, break your routine . . .)

_____
_____
_____
_____
_____
_____
_____

Happiness Highlights

Small
Smilables

Bonus! ☺ ☺ LOL!

Date _____

Su Mo Tu We Th Fr Sa

Stretch Day, The Sequel

Stretching your comfort zone

Write about your comfort zone stretching experiment.

_____

_____

_____

_____

_____

_____

_____

_____

_____

What can I do in the near future to stretch my comfort zone?

_____

_____

_____

_____

_____

_____

_____

_____

_____

Happiness Highlights

Small
Smilables

Bonus! 😊 😊 LOL!

Content

The message in "content" is:
Things are OK for me.

Think of a time you felt content and complete this "I" message.

I felt content when _____

_____

_____

because _____

_____

_____ .

Describe that situation or event.

_____

_____

_____

_____

_____

_____

Close your eyes and take yourself back to that event.
Notice the content feeling.
Breathe in that feeling as if you are breathing it in to the core of
you. From the core of you, let it spread out and fill you up.
Savor the feeling.

Happiness Highlights

Small
Smilables

Bonus! ☺ ☺ LOL!

Date _____

Content

List 3 times you felt content
(even if it was just a little content).

1. _____
2. _____
3. _____

What gets in the way of me feeling content?

_____

_____

_____

_____

_____

_____

_____

What would help me feel content?

_____

_____

_____

_____

_____

_____

_____

Happiness Highlights

Small
Smilables

Bonus! ☺ ☺ LOL!

Date _____

Game Day Word Search

Words can be forwards, backwards, up, down, or diagonal.

```
Z  B  X  T  Y  T  Y  W  D  Q  L  T  C  H
J  D  E  T  S  U  R  T  E  V  L  K  O  R
J  T  N  T  T  H  G  D  G  D  L  M  N  J
C  A  P  A  B  L  E  X  D  E  B  X  F  J
V  D  K  N  K  C  B  L  E  R  B  Q  I  K
C  E  R  D  L  T  X  Z  L  I  T  M  D  D
D  R  P  X  E  E  D  B  W  P  T  N  E  T
E  E  E  T  F  D  X  R  O  S  T  T  N  P
T  W  K  A  F  R  U  J  N  N  A  D  T  R
C  O  S  R  T  R  B  L  K  I  K  G  E  O
E  P  Z  N  N  I  N  M  C  X  Y  X  D  T
P  M  C  W  W  X  V  E  A  N  C  T  N  E
S  E  S  E  C  U  R  E  N  I  I  Q  H  C
E  L  U  F  E  P  O  H  T  C  T  W  M  T
R  N  T  Y  P  T  J  E  N  J  J  L  T  E
L  P  M  A  B  G  D  M  X  P  C  N  N  D
```

ACKNOWLEDGED	TRUSTED	PROTECTED	INCLUDED
CONFIDENT	SECURE	APPRECIATED	CREATIVE
EMPOWERED	SAFE	CAPABLE	INSPIRED
HOPEFUL	EXCITED	RESPECTED	

Happiness Highlights

Small
Smilables

Date _____

Check-in Day

Reflect back on what you've been learning
about upping your Happiness Quotient (HQ).

What are some HQ key points I've learned?

_____

_____

_____

_____

_____

What learning am I putting into action?

_____

_____

_____

_____

_____

My HQ-boosting plan moving forward:

_____

_____

_____

_____

_____

_____

Happiness Highlights

Small
Smilables

Bonus! ☺ ☺ LOL!

Passionate

The message in "passionate" is:
I've got strong feelings about this.

Think of a time you felt passionate and complete this "I" message.

I felt passionate when _____

_____

_____

because _____

_____

_____

Describe that situation or event.

_____

_____

_____

_____

_____

_____

Close your eyes and take yourself back to that event.
Notice the passionate feeling.
Breathe in that feeling as if you are breathing it in to the core of
you. From the core of you, let it spread out and fill you up.
Savor the feeling.

Happiness Highlights

Small
Smilables

68

Date _____

Passionate

List 3 times you felt passionate
(even if it was just a little passionate).

1. _____
2. _____
3. _____

Three things I feel passionate about:

1. _____
2. _____
3. _____

Pick one of your passions and write about how you can turn this passion into action.

My passion: _____

Turning it into action: _____

_____
_____
_____
_____
_____
_____
_____
_____
_____

Happiness Highlights

Small
Smilables

Bonus! LOL!

Reflection

"It is one of the most beautiful compensations
of this life that no one can sincerely try to help another
without helping himself."

– Charles Dudley

_____

_____

_____

_____

_____

_____

_____

_____

_____

_____

_____

_____

_____

Your mission for tomorrow,
should you decide to accept it,
is to help someone without helping yourself.

Happiness Highlights

Small
Smilables

Date _____

Su Mo Tu We Th Fr Sa

Reflection, Part Two

Helping Someone

My experience of trying to help someone:

_____

_____

_____

_____

_____

_____

_____

How can I try to help others in the future?

_____

_____

_____

_____

_____

_____

_____

_____

_____

_____

Happiness Highlights

Small
Smilables

 ☺ ☺ LOL!

71

Trusted

The message in "trusted" is:
Someone trusts me and believes in me.
They believe I'll be OK and do the right thing.

Think of a time you felt trusted and complete this "I" message.

I felt trusted when _____

_____

_____

because _____

_____

_____

Describe that situation or event.

_____

_____

_____

_____

_____

_____

Close your eyes and take yourself back to that event.
Notice the trusted feeling.
Breathe in that feeling as if you are breathing it in to the core of
you. From the core of you, let it spread out and fill you up.
Savor the feeling.

Happiness Highlights

Small
Smilables

Bonus!

LOL!

Date _____

Su Mo Tu We Th Fr Sa

Trusted

List 3 times you felt trusted
(even if it was just a little trusted).

1. _____
2. _____
3. _____

Make a general "I" message about feeling trusted.

I feel trusted when _____

_____

_____

because _____

_____

_____ .

Are there some changes I should make to be more worthy of people's trust?

_____

_____

_____

_____

_____

_____

_____

Happiness Highlights

Small
Smilables

Bonus! 😊 😆 LOL!

Stretch Day

Not everything that feels good is good for you

Are there some things I am drawn to for happiness that aren't good for me? (Like a 3rd piece of chocolate cake.)

_____

_____

_____

_____

Make an "I" message for a time you felt happy but it wasn't something good for you.

I felt happy when _____

_____

_____

because _____

_____

_____

If I'm drawn to something not good for me, what can I do to get my happiness in healthy ways instead?

_____

_____

_____

_____

Happiness Highlights

Small
Smilables

74

Date _____

Su Mo Tu We Th Fr Sa

Stretch Day, The Sequel

Not everything that feels good is good for you

What are some things that bring me happiness that are good for me?

_____

_____

_____

_____

_____

Make an "I" message for a time you felt happy and it was something good for you.

I felt happy when _____

_____

_____

because _____

_____

_____

What's one thing I can do tomorrow for a moment of healthy happy?

_____

_____

_____

_____

_____

Happiness Highlights

Small
Smilables

Date _____

Su Mo Tu We Th Fr Sa

Stimulated

The message in "stimulated" is:
My mental energy and interest are increased.

Think of a time you felt naturally stimulated (not by chemicals)
and complete this "I" message.

I felt stimulated when _____

_____

_____

because _____

_____

_____

Describe that situation or event.

_____

_____

_____

_____

_____

_____

Close your eyes and take yourself back to that event.
Notice the stimulated feeling.
Breathe in that feeling as if you are breathing it in to the core of
you. From the core of you, let it spread out and fill you up.
Savor the feeling.

Happiness Highlights

Small
Smilables

Date _____

Stimulated

List 3 times you felt stimulated
(even if it was just a little stimulated).

1. _____

2. _____

3. _____

Make a general "I" message about feeling stimulated.

I feel stimulated when _____

_____

_____

because _____

_____

_____

How can I get more of that energetic stimulated feeling from positive non-chemical sources in my life?

_____

_____

_____

_____

_____

_____

_____

Happiness Highlights

Small
Smilables

Bonus! ☺ ☺ LOL!

Game Day Word Search

Find the words on the right and reveal a hidden message. Words in the search can be forwards, backwards, up, down, or diagonal.

A	D	A	Y	L	U	F	E	P	O	H	W	I	T
H	O	U	D	T	S	U	F	N	S	H	I	D	N
E	I	S	S	E	L	I	A	K	E	Y	E	O	U
K	N	O	T	W	S	N	S	E	I	R	G	D	H
T	S	T	E	I	V	U	X	E	E	M	E	A	E
R	T	I	N	K	M	C	M	W	W	S	T	Y	V
C	D	G	Q	B	I	U	O	A	I	Y	R	P	I
O	M	P	G	T	M	P	L	R	M	W	W	M	T
N	R	X	E	M	M	R	P	A	Z	D	T	Q	A
T	T	D	Y	E	K	R	W	L	T	D	M	W	E
E	M	M	Z	M	U	T	F	G	D	E	M	N	R
N	K	V	L	S	P	L	N	K	P	Q	D	Q	C
T	P	A	S	S	I	O	N	A	T	E	M	L	Y

CREATIVE

CONTENT

PASSIONATE

EMPOWERED

EXCITED

HOPEFUL

STIMULATED

SURPRISED

SAFE

AMUSED

The letters for filling in the hidden message blanks are found in the word search by starting at the left top corner and going across the page line by line using the letters that are not part of the listed words—until the blanks in the hidden message are filled.

"___   ___   _____   _____

__   ____ , ___   ____ , _____ . "

___   _____   _____

Happiness Highlights

Small
Smilables

78

Date _____

Su Mo Tu We Th Fr Sa

Check-in Day

Reflect back on what you've been learning
about upping your Happiness Quotient (HQ).

What are some HQ key points I've learned?

_____
_____
_____
_____

_____

What learning am I putting into action?

_____
_____
_____
_____

_____

My HQ-boosting plan moving forward:

_____
_____
_____
_____
_____

_____

Happiness Highlights

Small
Smilables

Bonus! ☺ ☺ LOL!

Surprised

The message in "surprised" is:
Something unexpected has happened.
(This is about a good surprise.)

Think of a time you felt surprised (in a good way)
and complete this "I" message.

I felt surprised when _____

_____

_____

because _____

_____

_____ .

Describe that situation or event.

_____

_____

_____

_____

_____

Close your eyes and take yourself back to that event.
Notice the surprised feeling.
Breathe in that feeling as if you are breathing it in to the core of
you. From the core of you, let it spread out and fill you up.
Savor the feeling.

Happiness Highlights

Small
Smilables

Date _____

Su Mo Tu We Th Fr Sa

Surprised

List 3 times you felt surprised
(even if it was just a little surprised).

1. _____

2. _____

3. _____

What are your favorite surprises?

_____

_____

_____

_____

_____

_____

_____

Is there a small way you can surprise someone to give them a little boost? (flowers or a card, cup of coffee, take your partner on a date night, pay it forward . . .)

_____

_____

_____

_____

_____

Happiness Highlights

Small
Smilables

Bonus! ☺ ☺ LOL!

Reflection

"Your body hears everything your mind says."

– Naomi Judd

_____

_____

_____

_____

_____

_____

_____

_____

_____

_____

_____

_____

_____

_____

_____

Your mission for tomorrow,
should you decide to accept it,
is to notice what messages you tell yourself
and to note them in your journal.

Happiness Highlights

Small
Smilables

Date _____

Reflection, Part Two

My Self-talk

Messages I tell myself

_____
_____
_____
_____
_____
_____
_____

Positive messages to tell myself

_____
_____
_____
_____
_____
_____
_____
_____
_____
_____
_____

Happiness Highlights

Small
Smilables

Date _____
Su Mo Tu We Th Fr Sa

Acknowledged

The message in "acknowledged" is:
Someone paid attention to me or what I think.

Think of a time you felt acknowledged and complete this "I" message.

I felt acknowledged when _____

_____

_____

because _____

_____

_____ .

Describe that situation or event.

_____

_____

_____

_____

_____

_____

Close your eyes and take yourself back to that event.
Notice the acknowledged feeling.
Breathe in that feeling as if you are breathing it in to the core of
you. From the core of you, let it spread out and fill you up.
Savor the feeling.

Happiness Highlights

Small
Smilables

Date _____

Su Mo Tu We Th Fr Sa

Acknowledged

List 3 times you felt acknowledged
(even if it was just a little acknowledged).

1. _____

2. _____

3. _____

Make a general "I" message about feeling acknowledged.

I feel acknowledged when _____

_____

_____

because _____

_____

_____

How can I acknowledge myself?

_____

_____

_____

_____

_____

_____

_____

_____

Happiness Highlights

Small
Smilables

Bonus! ☺ ☺ LOL!

Stretch Day

Learning to take a compliment

Make an "I" message about when you get a compliment.

I feel _____ when I get a compliment because

_____

_____

_____

What messages do I hear in my head when I get a compliment?

_____

_____

_____

_____

_____

Follow-up question: If they are negative messages, how can you counter them?

_____

_____

_____

_____

_____

_____

_____

Happiness Highlights

Small
Smilables

Bonus! 😊 😄 LOL!

Stretch Day, The Sequel

Learning to take a compliment

You may need to develop the skill of taking in a compliment and letting it nurture you. If you're already good at it, you can enjoy this exercise too.

Describe a time you got a compliment—a genuine compliment that the person meant.

_____

_____

_____

_____

_____

_____

_____

_____

_____

_____

_____

_____

Close your eyes and take yourself back to that event.
Allow yourself to take in the acknowledged feeling.
Notice any negative self-talk and counter it.
Breathe in the complement as if you are breathing it in to the core of you.
Savor the feeling.

Happiness Highlights

Small
Smilables

Date _____
Su Mo Tu We Th Fr Sa

Attractive

The message in "attractive" is:
I look good.
(Note: Being attractive isn't just about what's on the outside, though it can be physical, it can also shine out from character.)

Think of a time you felt attractive and complete this "I" message.

I felt attractive when _____

_____

_____

because _____

_____

_____ .

Describe that situation or event.

_____

_____

_____

_____

_____

Close your eyes and take yourself back to that event.
Notice the attractive feeling.
Breathe in that feeling as if you are breathing it in to the core of you. From the core of you, let it spread out and fill you up.
Savor the feeling.

Happiness Highlights

Small
Smilables

88

Date _____

Attractive

List 3 times you felt attractive
(even if it was just a little attractive).

1. _____

2. _____

3. _____

What helps me feel attractive?

_____

_____

_____

_____

_____

_____

_____

My best physical features are:

1. _____

2. _____

3. _____

My best non-physical features are:

1. _____

2. _____

3. _____

Happiness Highlights

Small
Smilables

Bonus! ☺ ☺ LOL!

Game Day Scramble +

Unscramble the emotion words and enter letters from the unscrambled words into the number-corresponding boxes in the message.

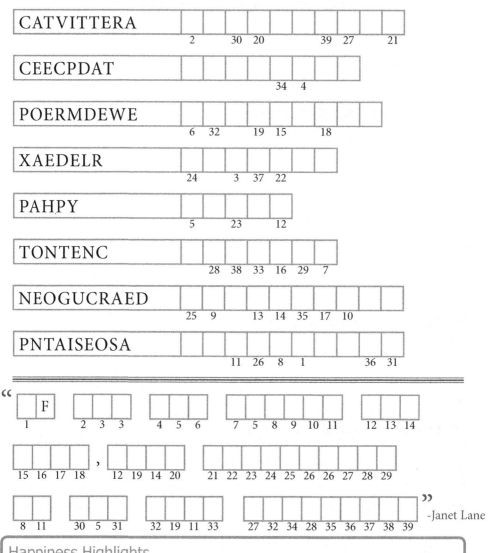

CATVITTERA
2   30   20   39   27   21

CEECPDAT
34   4

POERMDEWE
6   32   19   15   18

XAEDELR
24   3   37   22

PAHPY
5   23   12

TONTENC
28   38   33   16   29   7

NEOGUCRAED
25   9   13   14   35   17   10

PNTAISEOSA
11   26   8   1   36   31

"F
1   2 3 3   4 5 6   7 5 8 9 10 11   12 13 14

15 16 17 18 , 12 19 14 20   21 22 23 24 25 26 26 27 28 29

8 11   30 5 31   32 19 11 33   27 32 34 28 35 36 37 38 39 "

-Janet Lane

Happiness Highlights

Small
Smilables

90

Date _____

Check-in Day

Reflect back on what you've been learning
about upping your Happiness Quotient (HQ).

What are some HQ key points I've learned?

_____

_____

_____

_____

_____

What learning am I putting into action?

_____

_____

_____

_____

_____

My HQ-boosting plan moving forward:

_____

_____

_____

_____

_____

_____

Happiness Highlights

Small
Smilables

Bonus!

LOL!

Interested

The message in "interested" is:
I want to know about this.

Think of a time you felt interested and complete this "I" message.

I felt interested when _____

_____

_____

because _____

_____

_____ .

Describe that situation or event.

_____

_____

_____

_____

_____

_____

Close your eyes and take yourself back to that event.
Notice the interested feeling.
Breathe in that feeling as if you are breathing it in to the core of
you. From the core of you, let it spread out and fill you up.
Savor the feeling.

Happiness Highlights

Small
Smilables

Bonus! ☺ LOL!

Date _____

Su Mo Tu We Th Fr Sa

Interested

List 3 times you felt interested
(even if it was just a little interested).

1. _____

2. _____

3. _____

What is something that peaks my interest that I have not pursued but would like to?

_____

_____

_____

How can I pursue it?

_____

_____

_____

_____

_____

_____

_____

_____

_____

_____

Happiness Highlights

Small
Smilables

Bonus! ☺ 😊 LOL!

Date _____

Su Mo Tu We Th Fr Sa

Reflection

"Change your thoughts and you change your world."

– Norman Vincent Peale

_____

_____

_____

_____

_____

_____

_____

_____

_____

_____

_____

_____

_____

_____

Your mission for tomorrow,
should you decide to accept it,
is to notice your Downer Thoughts (DTs)
that get in the way of your happiness.

Happiness Highlights

Small
Smilables

Date _____

Reflection, Part Two

My Downer Thoughts (DTs)

Downer thoughts I noticed today (or see when I reflect back).

_____

_____

_____

_____

_____

_____

_____

_____

Replacing negative with positive

Downer Thought	Upper Replacement

Happiness Highlights

Small
Smilables

Bonus! ☺ ☺ LOL!

95

Date _____

Calm

The message in "calm" is:
I'm able to think clearly about the task at hand.

Think of a time you felt calm and complete this "I" message.

I felt calm when _____

_____

_____

because _____

_____

_____

Describe that situation or event.

_____

_____

_____

_____

_____

_____

Close your eyes and take yourself back to that event.
Notice the calm feeling.
Breathe in that feeling as if you are breathing it in to the core of
you. From the core of you, let it spread out and fill you up.
Savor the feeling.

Happiness Highlights

Small
Smilables

Date _____

Su Mo Tu We Th Fr Sa

Calm

List 3 times you felt calm
(even if it was just a little calm).

1. _____

2. _____

3. _____

Make a general "I" message about feeling calm.

I feel calm when _____

_____

_____

because _____

_____

_____

What does/might help me feel calm in challenging situations?

_____

_____

_____

_____

_____

_____

_____

_____

Happiness Highlights

Small
Smilables

Bonus! ☺ ☺ LOL!

Stretch Day

Relaxation skills

I'm going to teach you a few relaxation techniques to help you deal with stress and reduce anxiety.

#1 Take a couple of slow deep breaths.

With each breath in, breathe in relaxation.
With each breath out, breathe out tension.

#2 Relaxing phrase

Think of a word or phrase that helps you relax, i.e. "Relax." "It will be OK." "This too shall pass." "It is what it is." "You can do this."
There might be another word or phrase that is special to you and helps you relax as you take deep breaths.

What are some words or phrases that might help you relax?

_____

_____

_____

_____

_____

Practice using these simple relaxation skills.
Take a couple of deep breaths and think of
your relaxing word or phrase. Notice how you feel.

Happiness Highlights

Small
Smilables

Stretch Day, The Sequel

Another relaxation skill

#3 A "happy place."

Vividly think about something relaxing. It doesn't have to be a place and it doesn't have to be something you've experienced in real life. It could be a place you've been that was fun and/or relaxing, a scene out of a movie, a happy memory, a song, or an imaginary situation or place.

Vividly describe your happy place.
(include the sights, sounds, smells, what it feels like physically
and what it feels like emotionally)

_____

_____

_____

_____

_____

_____

_____

Practice using your happy place.
Close your eyes. Take a couple of deep breaths and think about
your happy place. Vividly imagine yourself there experiencing
your happy place. Notice the sights, sounds, smells, and feeling
of being in your happy place.

Happiness Highlights

Small
Smilables

Relaxed

The message in "relaxed" is:
I'm free of tension and stress.

Think of a time you felt relaxed and complete this "I" message.

I felt relaxed when _____

_____

_____

_____

because _____

_____

_____

Describe that situation or event.

_____

_____

_____

_____

_____

Close your eyes and take yourself back to that event.
Notice the relaxed feeling.
Breathe in that feeling as if you are breathing it in to the core of
you. From the core of you, let it spread out and fill you up.
Savor the feeling.

Happiness Highlights

Small
Smilables

Bonus! ☺ ☺ LOL!

Relaxed

List 3 times you felt relaxed
(even if it was just a little relaxed).

1. _____

2. _____

3. _____

Make a general "I" message about feeling relaxed.

I feel relaxed when _____

_____

_____

because _____

_____

_____

What helps me feel relaxed?

_____

_____

_____

_____

_____

_____

_____

Happiness Highlights

Small
Smilables

Bonus! ☺ ☺ LOL!

Game Day Crossword

Fill in the crossword by finding the emotion words from the list below that match each information clue.

DOWN

2. I'm not in danger.
4. Someone likes and cares about me.
6. There's a good chance this will work out well.
7. I really look forward to this or enjoy this.
8. I'm able to think clearly about the task at hand.
9. I feel good about who I am or what I have done.
10. Someone gets me or what I'm about.

ACROSS

1. I am able to do it on my own.
3. Someone likes me.
5. I'm free of tension and stress.

- ❏ ACCEPTED
- ❏ CALM
- ❏ EXCITED
- ❏ HOPEFUL
- ❏ INDEPENDENT
- ❏ LOVED
- ❏ PROUD
- ❏ RELAXED
- ❏ SAFE
- ❏ UNDERSTOOD

Happiness Highlights

Small Smilables

Date _____

Su Mo Tu We Th Fr Sa

Check-in Day

Reflect back on what you've been learning
about upping your Happiness Quotient (HQ).

What are some HQ key points I've learned?

_____
_____
_____
_____
_____

What learning am I putting into action?

_____
_____
_____
_____

My HQ-boosting plan moving forward:

_____
_____
_____
_____
_____

Happiness Highlights

Small
Smilables

Bonus! 😊 😊 LOL!

Valued

The message in "valued" is:
I'm important to someone or a group.

Think of a time you felt valued and complete this "I" message.

I felt valued when _____

_____

_____

because _____

_____

_____ .

Describe that situation or event.

_____

_____

_____

_____

_____

_____

Close your eyes and take yourself back to that event.
Notice the valued feeling.
Breathe in that feeling as if you are breathing it in to the core of
you. From the core of you, let it spread out and fill you up.
Savor the feeling.

Happiness Highlights

Small
Smilables

Date _____

Su Mo Tu We Th Fr Sa

Valued

List 3 times you felt valued
(even if it was just a little valued).

1. _____

2. _____

3. _____

What does it look like when someone values themselves?
(How do they act? How do they treat themselves?
How do they treat others?)

_____

_____

_____

_____

_____

_____

_____

Are there some ways that I should/could improve on how I value myself?

_____

_____

_____

_____

Happiness Highlights

Small
Smilables

Bonus! ☺ ☺ LOL!

Reflection

"Joy is a natural and inevitable benefit when we express our gifts and talents in the world."

– Anonymous

_____

_____

_____

_____

_____

_____

_____

_____

_____

_____

_____

_____

_____

Your mission for tomorrow,
should you decide to accept it,
is to think about and notice your gifts and talents
and how you express them to the world.

Happiness Highlights

Small
Smilables

Reflection, Part Two

My gifts and talents

gift/talent	how I express it to the world

What more can I do to express my gifts and talents to the world?

_____
_____
_____
_____
_____
_____
_____
_____

Happiness Highlights

Small
Smilables

Welcome

The message in "welcome" is:
I'm wanted here.

Think of a time you felt welcome and complete this "I" message.

I felt welcome when _____

_____

_____

because _____

_____

_____

Describe that situation or event.

_____

_____

_____

_____

_____

_____

Close your eyes and take yourself back to that event.
Notice the welcome feeling.
Breathe in that feeling as if you are breathing it in to the core of
you. From the core of you, let it spread out and fill you up.
Savor the feeling.

Happiness Highlights

Small
Smilables

Bonus! ☺ ☺ LOL!

Date ____________________
Su Mo Tu We Th Fr Sa

Welcome

List 3 times you felt welcome
(even if it was just a little welcome).

1. ____________________
2. ____________________
3. ____________________

Make a general "I" message about feeling welcome.

I feel welcome when ____________________
____
____

because ____________________
____
____________________.

What helps me feel welcome?

____
____
____
____
____
____
____
____

Happiness Highlights

Small Smilables

Stretch Day

Turn that frown upside down

Do you have resting frown face? Sometimes we're carrying around a frown and don't even realize it. Replacing that frown with a smile can give you a happiness boost.

What are some times throughout your day when you're doing things that are rather emotion-neutral?
(like working on the computer or doing the dishes or driving)

_____

_____

_____

_____

Close your eyes and practice a smile resting face.
Imagine yourself in one of the emotion-neutral scenarios and experience yourself catching that you are frowning and turn the frown into a smile.

What did you notice about the turn a frown into a smile practice?

_____

_____

_____

_____

Happiness Highlights

Small
Smilables

Bonus! ☺ ☺ LOL!

Date _____

Stretch Day, The Sequel

Advanced Turn that frown upside down

You can up your de-frowning even further. You can play with your response to negative thoughts like frustrations, annoyances, or thinking about somebody who did you wrong.

What are some reoccurring negative thoughts, frustrations or annoyances you have?

_____

_____

_____

_____

_____

_____

Close your eyes and practice turning the frown into a smile. Imagine yourself in one of the negative thoughts scenarios and experience yourself catching that you are frowning and turn the frown into a smile.

What did you notice about the turn a frown into a smile practice?

_____

_____

_____

_____

Happiness Highlights

Small
Smilables

Bonus!

LOL!

111

Liberated

The message in "liberated" is:
I'm free!

Think of a time you felt liberated and complete this "I" message.

I felt liberated when _____

_____

_____

because _____

_____

_____ .

Describe that situation or event.

_____

_____

_____

_____

_____

_____

_____

Close your eyes and take yourself back to that event.
Notice the liberated feeling.
Breathe in that feeling as if you are breathing it in to the core of
you. From the core of you, let it spread out and fill you up.
Savor the feeling.

Happiness Highlights

Small
Smilables

Bonus! ☺ LOL!

112

Date _____

Liberated

List 3 times you felt liberated
(even if it was just a little liberated).

1. _____

2. _____

3. _____

Is there anything that seems to bind me or hold me back?

_____

_____

_____

_____

_____

What might I do to free myself of something that binds me or holds me back?

_____

_____

_____

_____

_____

_____

_____

Happiness Highlights

Small
Smilables

Game Day Crossword

Fill in the crossword by finding the emotion words from the list on the next page that match each information clue. (Not all the emotion words listed are answers.)

DOWN

1. There's a good chance this will work out well.
3. I'm feeling more like I should or can do something than I did before.
5. Someone or something is keeping me safe.
6. Someone or something raised my spirits, helped me feel more like doing something.
8. Something or someone is somewhat funny.

ACROSS

2. Someone took my thoughts and feelings into account.
4. I'm able to think clearly about the task at hand.
7. I'm important to someone or a group.
9. Someone likes me.
10. Phew. I'm glad that didn't happen or is over.

Happiness Highlights

Small
Smilables

Date _____

Check-in Day

Reflect back on what you've been learning
about upping your Happiness Quotient (HQ).

What are some HQ key points I've learned?

_____

_____

_____

_____

_____

What learning am I putting into action?

_____

_____

_____

_____

My HQ-boosting plan moving forward:

_____

_____

_____

_____

_____

Crossword List
❑ ACCEPTED
❑ AMUSED
❑ CALM
❑ CONSIDERED
❑ ENCOURAGED
❑ EXCITED
❑ HOPEFUL
❑ INDEPENDENT
❑ INSPIRED
❑ LIBERATED
❑ LOVED
❑ PROTECTED
❑ PROUD
❑ RELAXED
❑ RELIEVED
❑ RESPECTED
❑ SAFE
❑ SATISFIED
❑ UNDERSTOOD
❑ VALUED

Happiness Highlights

Small
Smilables

Bonus! ☺ ☺ LOL!

Attracted

The message in "attracted" is:
I'm drawn to someone or something.

Think of a time you felt attracted and complete this "I" message.

I felt attracted to _____

_____

_____

because _____

_____

_____

Describe that situation or event.

_____

_____

_____

_____

_____

_____

Close your eyes and take yourself back to that event.
Notice the attracted feeling.
Breathe in that feeling as if you are breathing it in to the core of
you. From the core of you, let it spread out and fill you up.
Savor the feeling.

Happiness Highlights

Small
Smilables

Bonus! 😊 😄 LOL!

116

Date _____

Su Mo Tu We Th Fr Sa

Attracted

List 3 times you felt attracted
(even if it was just a little attracted).

1. _____

2. _____

3. _____

Make a general "I" message about feeling attracted to some<u>thing(s)</u>.

I feel attracted to _____

_____

_____

because _____

_____

_____

Make a general "I" message about feeling attracted to some<u>one(s)</u>.

I feel attracted to _____

_____

_____

because _____

_____

_____

Happiness Highlights

Small
Smilables

Bonus! ☺ ☺ LOL!

117

Date _____

Reflection

"No act of kindness, no matter how small,
is ever wasted."

– Aesop

_____

_____

_____

_____

_____

_____

_____

_____

_____

_____

_____

_____

_____

_____

Your mission for tomorrow,
should you decide to accept it,
is to perform a small act of kindness
and enter it into your journal.

Happiness Highlights

Small
Smilables

Reflection, Part Two

Act of kindness

My experience of attempting to perform a small act of kindness:

_____

_____

_____

_____

_____

_____

_____

_____

What acts of kindness could I do in the near future?

_____

_____

_____

_____

_____

_____

_____

_____

_____

Happiness Highlights

Small
Smilables

Bonus! ☺ ☺ LOL!

Proud

The message in "proud" is:
I feel good about who I am or what I have done.

Think of a time you felt proud and complete this "I" message.

I felt proud when _____

_____

_____

because _____

_____

_____

Describe that situation or event.

_____

_____

_____

_____

_____

_____

Close your eyes and take yourself back to that event.
Notice the proud feeling.
Breathe in that feeling as if you are breathing it in to the core of
you. From the core of you, let it spread out and fill you up.
Savor the feeling.

Happiness Highlights

Small
Smilables

Bonus! ☺ 😊 LOL!

Date _____

Proud

List 3 times you felt proud
(even if it was just a little proud).

1. _____

2. _____

3. _____

Many people have been taught that it is bad to be proud, but there are healthy levels of pride and over-the-top boastful levels. Healthy pride allows you to acknowledge your accomplishments and feel good about them.

What are the messages you have received about feeling proud?

_____

_____

_____

_____

_____

Can you think of examples of people who have healthy pride? What does it look like? What's the impact?

_____

_____

_____

_____

_____

_____

Happiness Highlights

Small
Smilables

Bonus! ☺ ☺ LOL!

Stretch Day

Perfectionism

"When your personal rule (spoken or unspoken) is that everything you need to do needs to be perfect,
failure is inevitable."

–Curt Rosengren,
U.S. News & World Report

How has perfectionism touched your life?

_____

_____

_____

_____

_____

_____

_____

_____

_____

_____

_____

_____

_____

_____

_____

_____

_____

Happiness Highlights

Small
Smilables

Bonus! ☺ ☺ LOL!

Stretch Day, The Sequel

Excellence

Perfectionism gets in the way of health and happiness. The truth is: you can't be perfect. Other people can't be perfect. Things can't go perfectly. Perfectionists are chronically frustrated, disappointed, overwhelmed, and anxious.

Excellence is a worthy goal. Perfection is not. Excellence is achieving to the best of your ability under the circumstances. Excellence allows for balancing of priorities and acknowledgement of the various aspects of each unique situation.

**How can you work on striving for excellence,
not perfection?**

_____

_____

_____

_____

_____

_____

_____

_____

_____

_____

_____

Happiness Highlights

Small
Smilables

Bonus! ☺ ☺ LOL!

123

Reassured

The message in "reassured" is:
I'm more sure of myself or my situation than I was.

Think of a time you felt reassured and complete this "I" message.

I felt reassured when _____

_____

_____

because _____

_____

_____.

Describe that situation or event.

_____

_____

_____

_____

_____

_____

Close your eyes and take yourself back to that event.
Notice the reassured feeling.
Breathe in that feeling as if you are breathing it in to the core of you. From the core of you, let it spread out and fill you up.
Savor the feeling.

Happiness Highlights

Small
Smilables

Bonus! ☺ ☺ LOL!

Date _____

Reassured

List 3 times you felt reassured
(even if it was just a little reassured).

1. _____
2. _____
3. _____

Make a general "I" message about feeling reassured.

I feel reassured when _____

_____

_____

because _____

_____

_____ .

What helps me feel reassured?

_____

_____

_____

_____

_____

_____

_____

_____

Happiness Highlights

Small
Smilables

Bonus! ☺ ☺ LOL!

125

Game Day Scramble +

Unscramble the emotion words and enter letters from the unscrambled words into the number-corresponding boxes in the message.

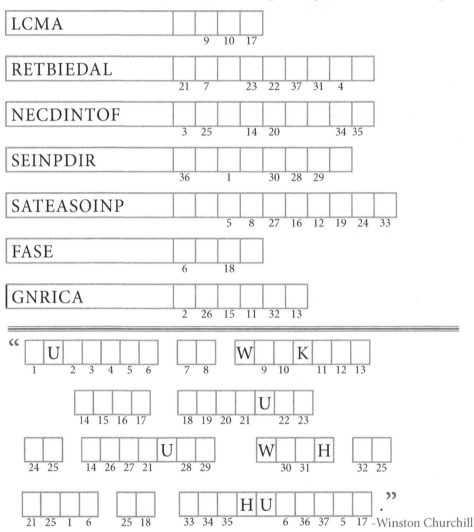

LCMA ☐☐☐
9 10 17

RETBIEDAL ☐☐ ☐☐☐☐ ☐
21 7 23 22 37 31 4

NECDINTOF ☐☐ ☐☐ ☐☐
3 25 14 20 34 35

SEINPDIR ☐ ☐ ☐☐☐
36 1 30 28 29

SATEASOINP ☐ ☐ ☐☐☐☐☐☐
5 8 27 16 12 19 24 33

FASE ☐ ☐
6 18

GNRICA ☐ ☐☐☐ ☐☐
2 26 15 11 32 13

"

☐U☐☐☐☐☐ ☐☐ W☐K☐☐☐
1 2 3 4 5 6   7 8   9 10 11 12 13

☐☐☐☐ ☐☐☐☐ U☐
14 15 16 17   18 19 20 21   22 23

☐☐ ☐☐☐U☐ ☐☐ W☐H ☐☐
24 25   14 26 27 21 28 29   30 31   32 25

☐☐☐☐ ☐☐ ☐☐☐HU☐☐☐☐☐ ".
21 25 1 6   25 18   33 34 35 6 36 37 5 17   -Winston Churchill

Happiness Highlights

Small
Smilables

126

Date _____

Su Mo Tu We Th Fr Sa

Check-in Day

Reflect back on what you've been learning
about upping your Happiness Quotient (HQ).

What are some HQ key points I've learned?

_____
_____
_____
_____
_____

What learning am I putting into action?

_____
_____
_____
_____

My HQ-boosting plan moving forward:

_____
_____
_____
_____
_____

Happiness Highlights

Small
Smilables

Bonus! ☺ ☺ LOL!

Respected

The message in "respected" is:
This person cares who I am and what I'm about.
This is a good person for me to be around.

Think of a time you felt respected and complete this "I" message.

I felt respected when _____

_____

_____

because _____

_____

_____ .

Describe that situation or event.

_____

_____

_____

_____

_____

Close your eyes and take yourself back to that event.
Notice the respected feeling.
Breathe in that feeling as if you are breathing it in to the core of
you. From the core of you, let it spread out and fill you up.
Savor the feeling.

Happiness Highlights

Small
Smilables

Bonus! ☺ LOL!

Date _____

Su Mo Tu We Th Fr Sa

Respected

List 3 times you felt respected
(even if it was just a little respected).

1. _____

2. _____

3. _____

Make a general "I" message about feeling respected.

I feel respected when _____

_____

_____

because _____

_____

_____

How do/should I show myself respect?

_____

_____

_____

_____

_____

_____

_____

_____

Happiness Highlights

Small
Smilables

129

Date _____

Reflection

"Anything worth doing
is worth doing poorly until you learn to do it well."

– Steve Brown

_____

_____

_____

_____

_____

_____

_____

_____

_____

_____

_____

_____

_____

_____

Your mission for tomorrow, should you decide
to accept it, is to try something new or take a
step in doing something you're not good at
and to note your experience in your journal.

Happiness Highlights

Small
Smilables

Date _____

Reflection, Part Two

My Challenge Op

My experience with trying something I'm not out-of-the-gate good at:

_____

_____

_____

_____

_____

_____

_____

_____

_____

My future plan for tackling new or challenging opportunities:

_____

_____

_____

_____

_____

_____

_____

Happiness Highlights

Small
Smilables

Bonus! ☺ ☺ LOL!

Capable

The message in "capable" is:
I can do this thing or lots of things.

Think of a time you felt capable and complete this "I" message.

I felt capable when _____

_____

because _____

_____

_____

Describe that situation or event.

_____

_____

_____

_____

_____

_____

Close your eyes and take yourself back to that event.
Notice the capable feeling.
Breathe in that feeling as if you are breathing it in to the core of
you. From the core of you, let it spread out and fill you up.
Savor the feeling.

Happiness Highlights

Small
Smilables

Bonus! ☺ LOL!

Date _____

Su Mo Tu We Th Fr Sa

Capable

List 3 times you felt capable
(even if it was just a little capable).

1. _____
2. _____
3. _____

Does anything get in the way of me feeling capable?

_____
_____
_____
_____
_____
_____
_____

What could help me feel more capable?

_____
_____
_____
_____
_____
_____
_____
_____

Happiness Highlights

Small
Smilables

Bonus! 🙂 😃 LOL!

133

Stretch Day

Challenging times offer learning opps

Think about a challenging time when you only realized afterward that you learned something from it.

Make an "I" message for what it felt like at the time.

(You can use the emotions list on page 4 to help label the emotion.)

I felt _____ when _____

_____

_____

because _____

_____

_____

What did you learn from the experience?

_____

_____

_____

_____

_____

_____

_____

_____

_____

_____

Happiness Highlights

Small
Smilables

134

Date _____

Su Mo Tu We Th Fr Sa

Stretch Day, The Sequel

Challenging times offer learning opps

Think about a challenging time when you realized you were learning something from it while it was happening.

Make an "I" message for what it felt like at the time.

I felt _____ when _____

_____

_____

because _____

_____

_____ .

What did you learn from the experience?

_____

_____

_____

_____

_____

_____

_____

_____

_____

_____

Happiness Highlights

Small
Smilables

Confident

The message in "confident" is:
I can do this thing or lots of things well.

Think of a time you felt confident and complete this "I" message.

I felt confident when _____

_____

_____

because _____

_____

_____ .

Describe that situation or event.

_____

_____

_____

_____

_____

_____

Close your eyes and take yourself back to that event.
Notice the confident feeling.
Breathe in that feeling as if you are breathing it in to the core of you. From the core of you, let it spread out and fill you up.
Savor the feeling.

Happiness Highlights

Small
Smilables

Bonus! LOL!

Date _____

Confident

List 3 times you felt confident
(even if it was just a little confident).

1. _____

2. _____

3. _____

Does anything get in the way of me feeling confident?

_____

_____

_____

_____

_____

_____

_____

How can I boost my confidence?

_____

_____

_____

_____

_____

_____

_____

Happiness Highlights

Small
Smilables

Bonus! ☺ ☺ LOL!

Game Day Crossword

Fill in the crossword by finding the emotion words from the list on the next page that match each information clue.

(Not all the emotion words listed are answers.)

ACROSS

2. I feel good about who I am or what I have done.
4. Someone paid attention to me or what I think.
7. I matter.
8. These people do and will back me up.
9. I am concerned about someone or something and want to help them.
10. I can do this thing or lots of things well.

DOWN

1. Something or someone is somewhat funny.
3. I've got strong feelings about this.
5. I appreciate something or someone.
6. Someone or something raised my spirits, helped me feel more like doing something.

Happiness Highlights

Small
Smilables

Check-in Day

Reflect back on what you've been learning
about upping your Happiness Quotient (HQ).

What are some HQ key points I've learned?

_____
_____
_____
_____
_____

What learning am I putting into action?

_____
_____
_____
_____

My HQ-boosting plan moving forward:

_____
_____
_____
_____
_____
_____

Crossword List

- ❏ ACCEPTED
- ❏ ACKNOWLEDGED
- ❏ AMUSED
- ❏ CALM
- ❏ CARING
- ❏ CONFIDENT
- ❏ CONSIDERED
- ❏ ENCOURAGED
- ❏ EXCITED
- ❏ GRATEFUL
- ❏ HOPEFUL
- ❏ IMPORTANT
- ❏ INDEPENDENT
- ❏ INSPIRED
- ❏ LIBERATED
- ❏ LOVED
- ❏ PASSIONATE
- ❏ PROTECTED
- ❏ PROUD
- ❏ RELAXED
- ❏ RELIEVED
- ❏ RESPECTED
- ❏ SAFE
- ❏ SATISFIED
- ❏ SUPPORTED
- ❏ UNDERSTOOD
- ❏ VALUED

Happiness Highlights

Small
Smilables

Bonus! ☺ ☺ LOL!

Grateful

The message in "grateful" is:
I appreciate something or someone.

Think of a time you felt grateful and complete this "I" message.

I felt grateful when _____

_____

_____

because _____

_____

_____

Describe that situation or event.

_____

_____

_____

_____

_____

_____

Close your eyes and take yourself back to that event.
Notice the grateful feeling.
Breathe in that feeling as if you are breathing it in to the core of
you. From the core of you, let it spread out and fill you up.
Savor the feeling.

Happiness Highlights

Small
Smilables

Bonus! ☺ 😊 LOL!

140

Date _____

Grateful

List 3 times you felt grateful
(even if it was just a little grateful).

1. _____
2. _____
3. _____

Some of the things I'm grateful for now

1. _____
2. _____
3. _____
4. _____
5. _____
6. _____
7. _____
8. _____
9. _____
10. _____
11. _____
12. _____
13. _____
14. _____
15. _____
16. _____

Happiness Highlights

Small
Smilables

Bonus! ☺ ☺ LOL!

Reflection

"Enjoy the little things,
for one day you may look back and realize
they were the big things.."

– Robert Brault

_____

_____

_____

_____

_____

_____

_____

_____

_____

_____

_____

_____

_____

Your mission for tomorrow,
should you decide to accept it,
is to notice little sources of happiness
and to note them in your journal.

Happiness Highlights

Small
Smilables

Date _____

Su Mo Tu We Th Fr Sa

Reflection, Part Two

Small Happies

Some of my small sources of happiness
—past, present and future.

1. _____
2. _____
3. _____
4. _____
5. _____
6. _____
7. _____
8. _____
9. _____
10. _____
11. _____
12. _____
13. _____
14. _____
15. _____
16. _____
17. _____
18. _____
19. _____

Happiness Highlights

Small
Smilables

Satisfied

The message in "satisfied" is:
Things are good enough.

Think of a time you felt satisfied and complete this "I" message.

I felt satisfied when _____

_____

_____

because _____

_____

_____ .

Describe that situation or event.

_____

_____

_____

_____

_____

_____

Close your eyes and take yourself back to that event.
Notice the satisfied feeling.
Breathe in that feeling as if you are breathing it in to the core of
you. From the core of you, let it spread out and fill you up.
Savor the feeling.

Happiness Highlights

Small
Smilables

Bonus! ☺ ☺ LOL!

144

Date _____

Satisfied

List 3 times you felt satisfied
(even if it was just a little satisfied).

1. _____
2. _____
3. _____

What gets in the way of me feeling satisfied?

_____
_____
_____
_____
_____
_____
_____

What would help me feel satisfied?

_____
_____
_____
_____
_____
_____
_____

Happiness Highlights

Small
Smilables

Bonus! ☺ ☺ LOL!

Stretch Day

Optimism

Optimism is having confidence in a positive outcome. Healthy optimism avoids the low end of the continuum (pessimism), and also the high end (being unrealistic).

It isn't about distorting the world by wearing rose-colored glasses. It's about believing that things may not go as planned but they will still be good, or at least OK, somehow.

Think of an example of someone (living or dead, famous or not)
who is pessimistic or unrealistic.
How has that attitude affected them and the people around them?

_____

_____

_____

_____

Think of an example of someone (living or dead, famous or not)
who is optimistic.
How has that attitude affected them and the people around them?

_____

_____

_____

_____

Happiness Highlights

Small
Smilables

Bonus! ☺ ☻ LOL!

Date _____

Su Mo Tu We Th Fr Sa

Stretch Day, The Sequel

Optimism

Pessimism   Unrealistic

**Where have you tended to land on the
pessimism--optimism--unrealistic continuum?
And how has that approach impacted your life?**

_____

_____

_____

_____

_____

_____

_____

**How could you improve your use of
the skill of optimism?** (Yes, it's a skill.)

_____

_____

_____

_____

_____

_____

_____

Happiness Highlights

Small
Smilables

Secure

The message in "secure" is:
I'm sure that things are going well for me
and will continue to go well.

Think of a time you felt secure and complete this "I" message.

I felt secure when _____

_____

_____

because _____

_____

_____ ,

Describe that situation or event.

_____

_____

_____

_____

_____

_____

Close your eyes and take yourself back to that event.
Notice the secure feeling.
Breathe in that feeling as if you are breathing it in to the core of
you. From the core of you, let it spread out and fill you up.
Savor the feeling.

Happiness Highlights

Small
Smilables

Bonus! ☺ ☺ LOL!

Date _____

Su Mo Tu We Th Fr Sa

Secure

List 3 times you felt secure
(even if it was just a little secure).

1. _____

2. _____

3. _____

What helps me feel secure?

_____

" is a .

is a .

How could optimism help me feel more secure?

is a .

is a .

is a .

Happiness Highlights

Whatever

. Choose wisely. "

Small
Smilables

–Roy Bennett, *The Light in* Bonus! ☺ ☺ LOL!

149

Game Day Word Finder

Fill in the word shapes from the word list to discover the message. (Not all the words listed are answers. Some words are used more than once.)

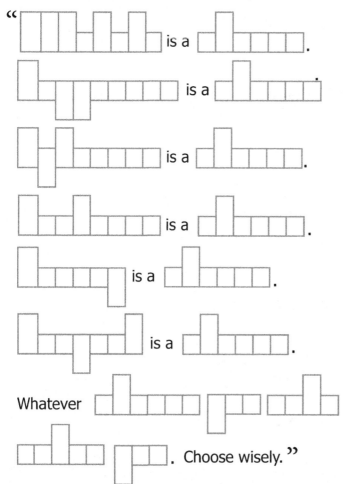

"_____ is a _____.

_____ is a _____.

_____ is a _____.

_____ is a _____.

_____ is a _____.

_____ is a _____.

Whatever _____ _____ _____

_____ _____. Choose wisely. "

–Roy Bennett, *The Light in the Heart*

Thought
Happiness
possibility
Smiling
takes
Kindness
make
Sadness
art
Opportunity
you
Respect
decision
makes
option
strength
Giving
choice
Attitude
possibility
Pessimism
skill
Optimism
take
Gratitude

Happiness Highlights

Small
Smilables

150

Date _____

Check-in Day

Reflect back on what you've been learning
about upping your Happiness Quotient (HQ).

What are some HQ key points I've learned?

_____
_____
_____
_____
_____

What learning am I putting into action?

_____
_____
_____
_____
_____

My HQ-boosting plan moving forward:

_____
_____
_____
_____
_____
_____

Happiness Highlights

Small
Smilables

Bonus! ☺ ☺ LOL!

Connected

The message in "connected" is:
I have something in common with this person (or people).

Think of a time you felt connected and complete this "I" message.

I felt connected when _____

_____

_____

because _____

_____

_____ .

Describe that situation or event.

_____

_____

_____

_____

_____

_____

Close your eyes and take yourself back to that event.
Notice the connected feeling.
Breathe in that feeling as if you are breathing it in to the core of
you. From the core of you, let it spread out and fill you up.
Savor the feeling.

Happiness Highlights

Small
Smilables

Bonus! ☺ ☺ LOL!

Date _____

Su Mo Tu We Th Fr Sa

Connected

List 3 times you felt connected
(even if it was just a little connected).

1. _____

2. _____

3. _____

Make a general "I" message about feeling connected.

I feel connected when _____

_____

_____

because _____

_____

_____

What can I do to feel more connected?

_____

_____

_____

_____

_____

_____

_____

_____

Happiness Highlights

Small
Smilables

Bonus! ☺ ☺ LOL!

Date _____

Reflection

"Release the joy that is inside of another,
and you release the joy that is inside of you."

– Neal Donald Walsch

_____

_____

_____

_____

_____

_____

_____

_____

_____

_____

_____

_____

_____

_____

Your mission for tomorrow,
should you decide to accept it,
is to try to "release the joy inside of another"
and write about the experience in your journal.

Happiness Highlights

Small
Smilables

Date _____

Su Mo Tu We Th Fr Sa

Reflection, Part Two

Joy-release Op

My experience of trying to release the joy in others:

_____

_____

_____

_____

_____

_____

_____

_____

_____

_____

My joy-release plan for tomorrow/future:

_____

_____

_____

_____

_____

_____

_____

_____

Happiness Highlights

Small
Smilables

Bonus! ☺ ☺ LOL!

Accepted

The message in "accepted" is:
Someone likes me.

Think of a time you felt accepted and complete this "I" message.

I felt accepted when _____

_____

_____

because _____

_____

_____ .

Describe that situation or event.

_____

_____

_____

_____

_____

_____

Close your eyes and take yourself back to that event.
Notice the accepted feeling.
Breathe in that feeling as if you are breathing it in to the core of
you. From the core of you, let it spread out and fill you up.
Savor the feeling.

Happiness Highlights

Small
Smilables

Date _____

Accepted

List 3 times you felt accepted
(even if it was just a little accepted).

1. _____
2. _____
3. _____

Make a general "I" message about feeling accepted.

I feel accepted when _____

_____

_____

because _____

_____

_____

What helps me feel accepted?

_____

_____

_____

_____

_____

_____

_____

_____

Happiness Highlights

Small
Smilables

Bonus! ☺ ☺ LOL!

157

Date _____

Stretch Day

Boosting self-acceptance

We can enjoy a rose at every stage of its development. When it's a bud, we aren't thinking, "Ick, you're ugly, inadequate and pathetic, if only you were in full bloom, I could enjoy you." No, we can enjoy it at every stage, even as we know that it will become bigger and more developed and more beautiful.

We are like that rose. We can accept ourselves, and enjoy who we are, even as we grow and develop and become something more.

My thoughts about self-acceptance:

_____

_____

_____

_____

_____

_____

_____

_____

Your mission for tomorrow, should you decide to accept it, is to notice a small way you can improve yourself and how you can accept yourself as you work on that change.

Happiness Highlights

Small
Smilables

Date _____

Su Mo Tu We Th Fr Sa

Stretch Day, The Sequel

Self-acceptance

Write about your experience of noticing
room for you to do something better
and how the whole self-acceptance thing worked out.

_____

_____

_____

_____

_____

_____

_____

How can I build on this experience in the future?

_____

_____

_____

_____

_____

_____

_____

_____

Happiness Highlights

Small
Smilables

Protected

The message in "protected" is:
Someone or something is keeping me safe.

Think of a time you felt protected and complete this "I" message.

I felt protected when _____

_____

_____

because _____

_____

_____

Describe that situation or event.

_____

_____

_____

_____

_____

_____

Close your eyes and take yourself back to that event.
Notice the protected feeling.
Breathe in that feeling as if you are breathing it in to the core of
you. From the core of you, let it spread out and fill you up.
Savor the feeling.

Happiness Highlights

Small
Smilables

Bonus! ☺ ☺ LOL!

160

Date _____

Su Mo Tu We Th Fr Sa

Protected

List 3 times you felt protected
(even if it was just a little protected).

1. _____

2. _____

3. _____

What helps me feel protected?

_____
_____
_____
_____
_____
_____
_____

What would help me feel protected as I stretch myself?

_____
_____
_____
_____
_____
_____
_____
_____

Happiness Highlights

Small
Smilables

Game Day Crossword

Fill in the crossword by finding the emotion words from the list on the next page that match each information clue. (Not all the words listed are answers.)

DOWN
1. I really want to do this.
3. I'm able to think clearly about the task at hand.
4. Something or someone has made me think "I can do it!"
5. I appreciate something or someone.
7. Phew. I'm glad that didn't happen or is over.

ACROSS
2. Someone likes me.
6. I feel good about who I am or what I have done.
8. Things are good enough.
9. I've got lots of ideas about how to do something.
10. I can do this thing or lots of things well.

Happiness Highlights

Small
Smilables

Date _____

Su Mo Tu We Th Fr Sa

Check-in Day

Reflect back on what you've been learning about upping your Happiness Quotient (HQ).

What are some HQ key points I've learned?

_____

_____

_____

_____

_____

What learning am I putting into action?

_____

_____

_____

_____

My HQ-boosting plan moving forward:

_____

_____

_____

_____

_____

Crossword List
- ❏ ACCEPTED
- ❏ ACKNOWLEDGED
- ❏ AMUSED
- ❏ APPRECIATED
- ❏ CALM
- ❏ CARING
- ❏ CONFIDENT
- ❏ CONSIDERED
- ❏ CREATIVE
- ❏ CURIOUS
- ❏ EMPOWERED
- ❏ ENCOURAGED
- ❏ ENTHUSIASTIC
- ❏ EXCITED
- ❏ GRATEFUL
- ❏ HOPEFUL
- ❏ IMPORTANT
- ❏ INDEPENDENT
- ❏ INSPIRED
- ❏ LIBERATED
- ❏ LOVED
- ❏ PASSIONATE
- ❏ PROTECTED
- ❏ PROUD
- ❏ RELAXED
- ❏ RELIEVED
- ❏ RESPECTED
- ❏ SAFE
- ❏ SATISFIED

Happiness Highlights

Small
Smilables

163

Date _____

Creative

The message in "creative" is:
I've got lots of ideas about how to do something.
(Note: Creativity isn't limited to artistic pursuits.)

Think of a time you felt creative and complete this "I" message.

I felt creative when _____

_____

_____

because _____

_____

_____ .

Describe that situation or event.

_____

_____

_____

_____

_____

_____

Close your eyes and take yourself back to that event.
Notice the creative feeling.
Breathe in that feeling as if you are breathing it in to the core of
you. From the core of you, let it spread out and fill you up.
Savor the feeling.

Happiness Highlights

Small
Smilables

Date _____

Creative

List 3 times you felt creative
(even if it was just a little creative).

1. _____

2. _____

3. _____

What helps me feel creative?

_____
_____
_____
_____
_____
_____
_____

How can I boost my creativity and my opportunities to use creativity?

_____
_____
_____
_____
_____
_____
_____

Happiness Highlights

Small
Smilables

Bonus! ☺ ☺ LOL!

165

Date _____

Reflection

"Play is the highest form of research."

– Albert Einstein

_____

_____

_____

_____

_____

_____

_____

_____

_____

_____

_____

_____

_____

_____

_____

Your mission for tomorrow,
should you decide to accept it,
is to find some moment(s) for "play" and to write about
your experience in your journal.

Happiness Highlights

Small
Smilables

Date _____

Reflection, Part Two

My Play Op

My experience of looking for moment(s) for play:

_____
_____
_____
_____
_____
_____
_____
_____

My play plan for tomorrow/future:

_____
_____
_____
_____
_____
_____
_____
_____
_____
_____

Happiness Highlights

Small
Smilables

Exhilarated

The message in "exhilarated" is:
I've got lots of emotional feel-good energy!

Think of a time you felt exhilarated and complete this "I" message.

I felt exhilarated when _____

_____

_____

because _____

_____

_____ .

Describe that situation or event.

_____

_____

_____

_____

_____

_____

Close your eyes and take yourself back to that event.
Notice the exhilarated feeling.
Breathe in that feeling as if you are breathing it in to the core of
you. From the core of you, let it spread out and fill you up.
Savor the feeling.

Happiness Highlights

Small
Smilables

Bonus! ☺ ☺ LOL!

168

Exhilarated

List 3 times you felt exhilarated
(even if it was just a little exhilarated).

1. _____

2. _____

3. _____

Make a general "I" message about feeling exhilarated.

I feel exhilarated when _____

_____

_____

because _____

_____

_____

How can I create opportunities to feel exhilarated?

_____

_____

_____

_____

_____

_____

_____

_____

Happiness Highlights

Small
Smilables

Bonus! ☺ ☺ LOL!

Date _____

Stretch Day

Laughing at yourself

When you can laugh at yourself, everywhere you go, wherever you are, you have a ready source of laughter.

I'm not encouraging you to make fun of yourself in a mean disparaging way. This is about laughing at silly mistakes, funny things that you do or say, and even things that frustrate you.

Write about your ability to laugh at yourself.

(How you do with the general concept. Events you can remember laughing about.)

_____

_____

_____

_____

_____

_____

_____

_____

_____

Your mission for tomorrow,
should you decide to accept it,
is to look for opportunities to laugh at yourself
and write about it into your journal.

Happiness Highlights

Small
Smilables

Date _____

Stretch Day, The Sequel

Laughing at yourself

How did you do with laughing at yourself today?

_____
_____
_____
_____
_____
_____
_____
_____
_____
_____
_____

How can you incorporate laughing at yourself into your life?

_____
_____
_____
_____
_____

Happiness Highlights

Small
Smilables

Bonus!

LOL!

171

Independent

The message in "independent" is:
I am able to do it on my own.

Think of a time you felt independent and complete this "I" message.

I felt independent when _____

_____

_____

because _____

_____

_____ .

Describe that situation or event.

_____

_____

_____

_____

_____

_____

Close your eyes and take yourself back to that event.
Notice the independent feeling.
Breathe in that feeling as if you are breathing it in to the core of
you. From the core of you, let it spread out and fill you up.
Savor the feeling.

Happiness Highlights

Small
Smilables

Bonus! ☺ ☺ LOL!

Date _____

Independent

List 3 times you felt independent
(even if it was just a little independent).

1. _____

2. _____

3. _____

Make a general "I" message about feeling independent.

I feel independent when _____

_____

_____

because _____

_____

_____

How can I balance independence and my relationships (with a partner, family, co-workers, friends...)?

_____

_____

_____

_____

_____

_____

_____

Happiness Highlights

Small
Smilables

Bonus! ☺ ☺ LOL!

173

Date _____

Su Mo Tu We Th Fr Sa

Game Day Crossword

Fill in the crossword by finding the emotion words from the list on the next page that match each information clue. (Not all the words listed are answers.)

DOWN

2. I really look forward to this or enjoy this.
3. Things are OK for me.
4. Things are good enough.
5. I'm sure that things are going well for me and will continue to go well.

ACROSS

1. Someone cares about me and is helping me be the best I can be.
3. I am concerned about someone or something and want to help them.
6. Someone or something is keeping me safe.
7. I'm feeling more like I should or can do something than I did before.
8. I'm not in danger.
9. I want to know about this.

Happiness Highlights

Small
Smilables

174

Date _____

Su Mo Tu We Th Fr Sa

Check-in Day

Reflect back on what you've been learning about upping your Happiness Quotient (HQ).

What are some HQ key points I've learned?

_____

_____

_____

_____

_____

What learning am I putting into action?

_____

_____

_____

_____

_____

My HQ-boosting plan moving forward:

_____

_____

_____

_____

_____

_____

Crossword List

- ❏ ACCEPTED
- ❏ AMUSED
- ❏ APPRECIATED
- ❏ CALM
- ❏ CARING
- ❏ CONFIDENT
- ❏ CONSIDERED
- ❏ CONTENT
- ❏ CREATIVE
- ❏ CURIOUS
- ❏ EMPOWERED
- ❏ ENCOURAGED
- ❏ ENTHUSIASTIC
- ❏ EXCITED
- ❏ GRATEFUL
- ❏ HOPEFUL
- ❏ IMPORTANT
- ❏ INDEPENDENT
- ❏ INSPIRED
- ❏ INTERESTED
- ❏ LIBERATED
- ❏ LOVED
- ❏ NURTURED
- ❏ PROTECTED
- ❏ PROUD
- ❏ RELAXED
- ❏ RESPECTED
- ❏ SAFE
- ❏ SATISFIED
- ❏ SECURE

Happiness Highlights

Small
Smilables

175

Considered

The message in "considered" is:
Someone took my thoughts and feelings into account.

Think of a time you felt considered and complete this "I" message.

I felt considered when _____

_____

_____

because _____

_____

_____ '

Describe that situation or event.

_____

_____

_____

_____

_____

_____

Close your eyes and take yourself back to that event.
Notice the considered feeling.
Breathe in that feeling as if you are breathing it in to the core of
you. From the core of you, let it spread out and fill you up.
Savor the feeling.

Happiness Highlights

Small
Smilables

Date _____

Su Mo Tu We Th Fr Sa

Considered

List 3 times you felt considered
(even if it was just a little considered).

1. _____

2. _____

3. _____

Make a general "I" message about feeling considered.

I feel considered when _____

_____

_____

because _____

_____

_____

Can I do a better job balancing considering others and considering myself?

_____

_____

_____

_____

_____

_____

Happiness Highlights

Small
Smilables

Bonus! ☺ 😊 LOL!

Reflection

"Sometimes your joy is the source of your smile,
but sometimes your smile can be the source of your joy. "

– Thich Nhat Hanh

_____
_____
_____
_____
_____
_____
_____
_____
_____
_____
_____
_____
_____

Your mission for tomorrow,
should you decide to accept it,
is to notice your self-started bonus smiles and
joy-started smiles and to write about them in your journal.

Happiness Highlights

Small
Smilables

Reflection, Part Two

My smiles

My joy-started smiles:

_____

_____

_____

_____

_____

_____

_____

_____

_____

My bonus smiles:

_____

_____

_____

_____

_____

_____

_____

_____

_____

_____

Happiness Highlights

Small
Smilables

Important

The message in "important" is:
I matter.

Think of a time you felt important and complete this "I" message.

I felt important when _____

_____

_____

because _____

_____

_____ .

Describe that situation or event.

_____

_____

_____

_____

_____

_____

Close your eyes and take yourself back to that event.
Notice the important feeling.
Breathe in that feeling as if you are breathing it in to the core of
you. From the core of you, let it spread out and fill you up.
Savor the feeling.

Happiness Highlights

Small
Smilables

Bonus! ☺ ☺ LOL!

Date _____

Su Mo Tu We Th Fr Sa

Important

List 3 times you felt important
(even if it was just a little important).

1. _____

2. _____

3. _____

What gets in the way of me feeling important?

_____
_____
_____
_____
_____
_____
_____

What helps me feel important?

_____
_____
_____
_____
_____
_____
_____
_____

Happiness Highlights

Small
Smilables

Bonus! ☺ ☺ LOL!

Stretch Day

Serenity

May I have the serenity to accept the things I cannot change,
the courage to change the things I can,
and the wisdom to know the difference.

–adapted from a prayer by Reinhold Niebuhr

"Serenity now."

–Frank Costanza (Seinfeld episode)

What are some things that I can't change and would do well to accept?

_____

_____

_____

_____

_____

Follow-up question: What would help me accept these things?

_____

_____

_____

_____

_____

_____

_____

_____

Happiness Highlights

Small
Smilables

Bonus! ☺ ☺ LOL!

Date _____

Stretch Day, The Sequel

Serenity

What are some things I can change?

_____

_____

_____

_____

_____

_____

_____

Follow-up question: What are some steps I can take to help those changes happen?

_____

_____

_____

_____

_____

_____

_____

_____

_____

_____

Happiness Highlights

Small
Smilables

Trusting

The message in "trusting" is:
This is someone or something I can trust and believe in to be OK and do the right thing.

Think of a time you felt trusting and complete this "I" message.

I felt trusting when _____

_____

_____

because _____

_____

_____

Describe that situation or event.

_____

_____

_____

_____

_____

Close your eyes and take yourself back to that event.
Notice the trusting feeling.
Breathe in that feeling as if you are breathing it in to the core of you. From the core of you, let it spread out and fill you up.
Savor the feeling.

Happiness Highlights

Small
Smilables

184

Date _____

Trusting

List 3 times you felt trusting
(even if it was just a little trusting).

1. _____

2. _____

3. _____

Make a general "I" message about feeling trusting.

I feel trusting when _____

_____

_____

because _____

_____

_____

What helps me feel trusting?

_____

_____

_____

_____

_____

_____

_____

Happiness Highlights

Small
Smilables

Bonus! ☺ ☺ LOL!

Game Day Cryptogram

Crack the code to fill in the blanks and reveal a quote from Frank Crane's book, *Four Minute Essays*, written in 1919.

A	B	C	D	E	F	G	H	I	L	M	N	O	P	R	S	T	U	V
17				21			16	14							18			

"　　H E 　　　 A 　　　 I S 　　 H A
　 20 16 21　 19 17 12 20　 14 18　 20 16 17 20

H A 　　 I 　 E S S 　　　 E S
16 17 5 5 14 3 21 18 18　 1 8 21 18　 3 8 20

　　　　 E 　　　　　　 H E 　　 I
12 8 9 21　 19 15 8 9　 20 16 21　 13 14 26

E 　 E 　　 S 　　　　 I 　 E
21 22 21 3 20 18　 8 19　 25 14 19 21　 13 10 20

I S 　　 A 　 E 　　　　　　　
14 18　 9 17 1 21　 10 5　 8 19 '

I 　　　　 E 　 A 　 E 　 I 　　　 E
14 3 3 10 9 21 15 17 13 25 21　 25 14 20 20 25 21

　 H I 　　 S 。"
20 16 14 3 26 18

Happiness Highlights

Small
Smilables

Date _____

Check-in Day

Reflect back on what you've been learning
about upping your Happiness Quotient (HQ).

What are some HQ key points I've learned?

_____

_____

_____

_____

_____

What learning am I putting into action?

_____

_____

_____

_____

My HQ-boosting plan moving forward:

_____

_____

_____

_____

_____

Happiness Highlights

Small
Smilables

Bonus! ☺ ☺ LOL!

Loved

The message in "loved" is:
Someone likes and cares about me.

Think of a time you felt loved and complete this "I" message.

I felt loved when _____

_____

_____

because _____

_____

_____

Describe that situation or event.

_____

_____

_____

_____

_____

_____

Close your eyes and take yourself back to that event.
Notice the loved feeling.
Breathe in that feeling as if you are breathing it in to the core of you. From the core of you, let it spread out and fill you up.
Savor the feeling.

Happiness Highlights

Small
Smilables

Date _____

Su Mo Tu We Th Fr Sa

Loved

List 3 times you felt loved
(even if it was just a little loved).

1. _____

2. _____

3. _____

Make a general "I" message about feeling loved.

I feel loved when _____

_____

_____

because _____

_____

_____

How do I like to be loved? (ie with flowers and candy, listening to me, support, appreciation, valuing my opinion, breakfast in bed, telling me directly, accepting me...)

_____

_____

_____

_____

_____

_____

_____

Happiness Highlights

Small
Smilables

Bonus! 😊 😋 LOL!

189

Date _____

Reflection

"Well-ordered self-love is right and natural."

– Saint Thomas Aquinas

_____

_____

_____

_____

_____

_____

_____

_____

_____

_____

_____

_____

_____

_____

_____

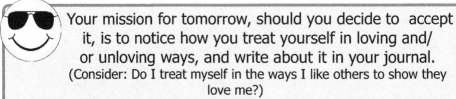

Your mission for tomorrow, should you decide to accept it, is to notice how you treat yourself in loving and/ or unloving ways, and write about it in your journal.
(Consider: Do I treat myself in the ways I like others to show they love me?)

Happiness Highlights

Small
Smilables

Reflection, Part Two

Loving myself

Loving ways I treat myself:

_____
_____
_____
_____
_____

Unloving ways I treat myself:

_____
_____
_____

How can I treat myself in a lovingly-balanced way in the future?

_____
_____
_____
_____
_____
_____
_____
_____

Happiness Highlights

Small
Smilables

Bonus! ☺ ☺ LOL!

Nurtured

The message in "nurtured" is:
Someone cares about me
and is helping me be the best I can be.

Think of a time you felt nurtured and complete this "I" message.

I felt nurtured when _____

_____

_____

because _____

_____

_____ .

Describe that situation or event.

_____

_____

_____

_____

_____

_____

Close your eyes and take yourself back to that event.
Notice the nurtured feeling.
Breathe in that feeling as if you are breathing it in to the core of
you. From the core of you, let it spread out and fill you up.
Savor the feeling.

Happiness Highlights

Small
Smilables

Date _____

Nurtured

List 3 times you felt nurtured
(even if it was just a little nurtured).

1. _____
2. _____
3. _____

How can/do I nurture others?

_____
_____
_____
_____
_____
_____
_____

How can/do I nurture myself?

_____
_____
_____
_____
_____
_____
_____

Happiness Highlights

Small
Smilables

Bonus! ☺ ☺ LOL!

Stretch Day

Finding the good in bad

There is usually some "good" in "bad" situations even if it's difficult to see at the time. Finding the good in bad doesn't require you to pretend that it's all good. You need to acknowledge the emotional discomfort, challenges, and downsides to difficulties. And, you may also benefit from seeing their silver lining.

What are some benefits to seeing the silver lining in life's clouds?

_____

_____

_____

What opportunity could lie in each of these potential difficulties?

"Bad" thing	Potential "good"
hitting 3 red lights in a row	
choosing the slow line in the grocery store	
breaking a leg	
losing a job	

Happiness Highlights

Small
Smilables

Bonus! ☺ ☺ LOL!

194

Date _____

Su Mo Tu We Th Fr Sa

Stretch Day, The Sequel

Finding the good in bad

Write about a difficulty in your life that you gained something from.
(It offered a change in direction, growth, or other benefit.)

_____

_____

_____

_____

_____

_____

_____

Write about a difficulty you are facing now or expect in the future
and the potential silver lining to that challenge.

_____

_____

_____

_____

_____

_____

_____

_____

Happiness Highlights

Small
Smilables

Bonus! ☺ ☺ LOL!

Appreciated

The message in "appreciated" is:
Someone noticed and is grateful for what I did.

Think of a time you felt appreciated and complete this "I" message.

I felt appreciated when _____

_____

_____

because _____

_____

_____ .

Describe that situation or event.

_____

_____

_____

_____

_____

_____

Close your eyes and take yourself back to that event.
Notice the appreciated feeling.
Breathe in that feeling as if you are breathing it in to the core of
you. From the core of you, let it spread out and fill you up.
Savor the feeling.

Happiness Highlights

Small
Smilables

Bonus! ☺ ☺ LOL!

Date _____

Su Mo Tu We Th Fr Sa

Appreciated

List 3 times you felt appreciated
(even if it was just a little appreciated).

1. _____
2. _____
3. _____

Some of the things I appreciate in others

1. _____
2. _____
3. _____
4. _____
5. _____
6. _____
7. _____

Some of the things I appreciate in myself

1. _____
2. _____
3. _____
4. _____
5. _____
6. _____
7. _____

Happiness Highlights

Small
Smilables

197

Game Day Stair Master

Starting at the bottom left, find your way to the top right roof for your Ta-da! Note: Sometimes you have to go down before you can go up.

Happiness Highlights

Small
Smilables

198

Date _____

Su Mo Tu We Th Fr Sa

Check-in Day

Reflect back on what you've been learning
about upping your Happiness Quotient (HQ).

What are some HQ key points I've learned?

_____
_____
_____
_____
_____

What learning am I putting into action?

_____
_____
_____
_____

My HQ-boosting plan moving forward:

_____
_____
_____
_____
_____

Happiness Highlights

Small
Smilables

Understood

The message in "understood" is:
Someone gets me or what I'm about.

Think of a time you felt understood and complete this "I" message.

I felt understood when _____

_____

_____

because _____

_____

_____ .

Describe that situation or event.

_____

_____

_____

_____

_____

_____

Close your eyes and take yourself back to that event.
Notice the understood feeling.
Breathe in that feeling as if you are breathing it in to the core of
you. From the core of you, let it spread out and fill you up.
Savor the feeling.

Happiness Highlights

Small
Smilables

Bonus! ☺ ☺ LOL!

Date _____

Su Mo Tu We Th Fr Sa

Understood

List 3 times you felt understood
(even if it was just a little understood).

1. _____

2. _____

3. _____

What is one thing I would like to feel understood about?

_____

_____

_____

_____

_____

_____

_____

Some things I understand about myself:

_____

_____

_____

_____

_____

_____

_____

_____

Happiness Highlights

Small
Smilables

Bonus! ☺ ☺ LOL!

Date _____

Su Mo Tu We Th Fr Sa

Reflection

"Don't ask what the world needs.
Ask what makes you come alive, and go do it.
Because what the world needs is people who have come alive."

– Howard Thurman

_____

_____

_____

_____

_____

_____

_____

_____

_____

_____

_____

_____

_____

Your mission for tomorrow,
should you decide to accept it,
is to notice what makes you "come alive"
and write about it in your journal.

Happiness Highlights

Small
Smilables

Date _____

Reflection, Part Two

What makes me come alive

What makes me come alive?

_____

_____

_____

_____

_____

What can I do with what makes me come alive?

_____

_____

_____

_____

Follow-up question: What would help me do it?

_____

_____

_____

_____

_____

_____

Happiness Highlights

Small
Smilables

Supported

The message in "supported" is:
These people do and will back me up.

Think of a time you felt supported and complete this "I" message.

I felt supported when _____

_____

_____

because _____

_____

_____

Describe that situation or event.

_____

_____

_____

_____

_____

Close your eyes and take yourself back to that event.
Notice the supported feeling.
Breathe in that feeling as if you are breathing it in to the core of
you. From the core of you, let it spread out and fill you up.
Savor the feeling.

Happiness Highlights

Small
Smilables

Date _____

Su Mo Tu We Th Fr Sa

Supported

List 3 times you felt supported
(even if it was just a little supported).

1. _____
2. _____
3. _____

How do/can I support others?

_____
_____
_____
_____
_____
_____

How do/can I support myself?

_____
_____
_____
_____
_____
_____

Happiness Highlights

Small
Smilables

Bonus! ☺ ☺ LOL!

Stretch Day

Plan for joy

"Joy does not simply happen to us.
We have to choose joy and keep choosing it every day."

– Henri Nouwen

My joy mission statement:

_____

_____

_____

_____

Possible ways to have joy daily:

_____

_____

_____

_____

_____

_____

_____

_____

_____

_____

_____

Happiness Highlights

Small
Smilables

Bonus! ☺ ☺ LOL!

Date _____

Stretch Day, The Sequel

My joy plan

_____

_____

_____

_____

_____

_____

_____

_____

_____

_____

_____

_____

_____

_____

_____

_____

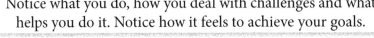

Visualize your plan in action.
Close your eyes and experience yourself going through
a day putting your plan into action.
Notice what you do, how you deal with challenges and what
helps you do it. Notice how it feels to achieve your goals.

Happiness Highlights

Small
Smilables

Hopeful

The message in "hopeful" is:
There's a good chance this will work out well.

Think of a time you felt hopeful and complete this "I" message.

I felt hopeful when _____

_____

_____

because _____

_____

_____ .

Describe that situation or event.

_____

_____

_____

_____

_____

_____

Close your eyes and take yourself back to that event.
Notice the hopeful feeling.
Breathe in that feeling as if you are breathing it in to the core of
you. From the core of you, let it spread out and fill you up.
Savor the feeling.

Happiness Highlights

Small
Smilables

Bonus! ☺ ☺ LOL!

208

Date _____

Su Mo Tu We Th Fr Sa

Hopeful

List 3 times you felt hopeful
(even if it was just a little hopeful).

1. _____

2. _____

3. _____

I feel hopeful about:

_____

_____

_____

_____

_____

_____

_____

_____

_____

_____

_____

_____

_____

_____

_____

_____

_____

Happiness Highlights

Small
Smilables

Bonus! ☺ ☺ LOL!

Graduation

**Congratulations!
You made it to the end!
You graduated with honors!**
(or should that be with humors?)

Graduation

Game Day Answers

Game Day Answers

Page 18

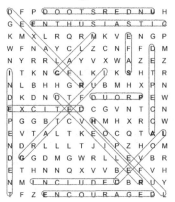

Page 30

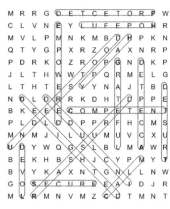

Page 42

1. "Laughing deeply is <u>living</u> deeply." – Milan Kundera
2. "If it feels good to laugh then <u>laugh</u> to feel good." – Mike Moore
3. "Laughter is a gift from nature. It's good for us. It's <u>free</u>, easy to <u>carry</u> around and we can <u>share</u> it with anyone." – Jeffrey Briar
4. "It is bad to <u>suppress</u> laughter. It goes back down and spreads to your <u>hips</u>." –Fred Allen
5. "Laughter is like changing a baby's <u>diaper</u>—it doesn't permanently solve any problems, <u>but</u> it makes things more <u>tolerable</u> for a while." –Unclaimed

Page 54

Page 66

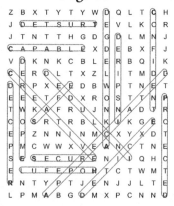

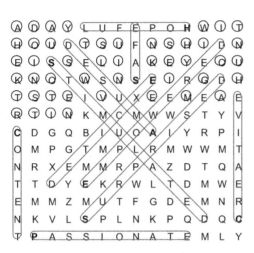

Page 78

"A day without sunshine is like, you know, night."
-Steve Martin
Word Search Hidden Message

Page 90

ATTRACTIVE
ACCEPTED
EMPOWERED
RELAXED
HAPPY
CONTENT
ENCOURAGED
PASSIONATE

"Of all the things you wear, your expression is the most important." — Janet Lane

Page 102

Page 114

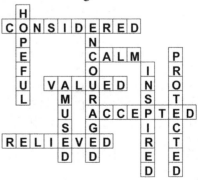

Game Day Answers

Page 126

CALM
LIBERATED
CONFIDENT
INSPIRED
PASSIONATE
SAFE
CARING

"Success is walking from failure to failure with no loss of enthusiasm."
-Winston Churchill

Page 138

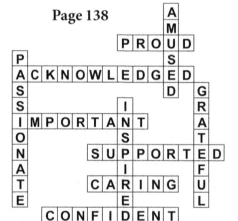

Page 150

"Attitude is a choice.
Happiness is a choice.
Optimism is a choice.
Kindness is a choice.
Giving is a choice.
Respect is a choice.
Whatever choice you make
makes you. Choose wisely."
-Roy T. Bennett,
The Light in the Heart

Page 162

Page 174

216

Page 186

A	B	C	D	E	F	G	H	I	L	M	N	O	P	R	S	T	U	V
17	13	12	1	21	19	26	16	14	25	9	3	8	5	15	18	20	10	22

From a 1919 book, "Four Minute Essays", by Frank Crane:

"Happiness is rarely visible to the multitude, says a shrewd observer; it lies hidden in odd corners and quiet places. . .

<u>The fact is that happiness does not come from the big events of life, but is made up of innumerable little things</u>. Ordinary everyday happiness is composed of shoes that fit, stomach that digests, purse that does not flatten, a little appreciation, and a bit of this, that, and the other, . . .

Note all the pleasurable things. For instance, a good sleep, a delightful snooze in bed after you ought to get up, a delicious bath, the invigorating caress of cold water, a good breakfast, with somebody you love visible across the coffee-cups, a half-hour's diversion with the newspaper, the flash of nature's loveliness outdoors as you go to work, interesting faces on the streetcar, pleasures of your business, pleasant relations with your fellow-workers, meeting old friends and new faces, the good story someone tells you . . ."

Page 198

About the author

Ann Silvers, MA
Counselor, Relationship Coach, Hypnotherapist and Author

I haven't always been a counselor. During my first career, I was a Medical Lab Tech working in Microbiology labs in a couple of large hospitals in Canada. When I was pregnant with my first child, I dove into learning everything I could about parenting because I didn't want to parent the way I was parented. (I was raised by two alcoholics.) A big part of my learning focused on communication and emotion skills.

When my children were young, two things happened that set my course toward a counseling career: I was invited to teach a local counselor's parenting class and I had my own childhood therapy. I decided that when I was ready to return to the paid work force, I wanted to work with humans, not microorganisms. I wanted to help other people experience the positive changes I felt from my own therapy and self-help discoveries.

So—while I took advantage of opportunities to teach communication and relationship skills workshops, I went back to school to get degrees in psychology and counseling. (By that time, I had moved with my family to the Seattle area in the US.)

Over decades of working with people in groups, and as individuals and couples, I developed ways of explaining concepts and created exercise materials that I eventually turned into card sets, books, and recordings for publication so that more people could benefit from the products that are the result of years of experimenting with using and improving.

You can find me on social media and annsilvers.com (eStore and blog).

Made in the USA
Middletown, DE
18 September 2020